Finding Peace Within Shattered Pieces — Healing Trauma with Yoga and Meditation

BY SIMRANJEET KAUR

Solstice 2022

So glad we're on this journey together!

Love, Tonya

Finding Peace Within Shattered Pieces – Healing Trauma with Yoga and Meditation

BY SIMRANJEET KAUR

BY SIMRANJEET KAUR (JACKIE WAKEFORD-SMITH)

PUBLISHED BY THE KUNDALINI RESEARCH INSTITUTE

TRAINING • PUBLISHING • RESEARCH • RESOURCES

PO BOX 1819 SANTA CRUZ, NM 87532

WWW.KUNDALINIRESEARCHINSTITUTE.ORG

ISBN: 978-0-9639847-9-1

MANAGING EDITOR: MARIANA LAGE (HARISHABAD KAUR)

CONSULTING EDITOR: AMRIT SINGH KHALSA

DESIGN: FERNANDA MONTE-MÓR

LAYOUT: CAROLINE GISCHEWSKI

ILLUSTRATOR: JANIS SOUZA

LINE EDITOR: RAINER PERRY

PROOFREADING: ONG KAR KAUR KHALSA

REVIEWER: SIRI NEEL KAUR KHALSA AND DIANA NANU

EDITORIAL ASSISTANTS: ANTÔNIO LARA SILVA AND WASHINGTON DA SELVA

—

The diet, exercise and lifestyle suggestions in this book come from ancient yogic traditions. Nothing in this book should be construed as medical advice. Neither the author nor the publisher shall be liable or responsible for any loss, injury, damage, allegedly arising from any information or suggestion in this book. The benefits attributed to the practice of Kundalini Yoga and meditation stem from centuries-old yogic tradition. Results will vary with individuals. Always check with your personal physician or licensed care practitioner before making any significant modification in your diet or lifestyle, to ensure that the lifestyle changes are appropriate for your personal health condition and consistent with any medication you may be taking.

This publication has received the KRI Seal of Approval. This Seal is given only to products that have been reviewed for accuracy and integrity of the sections containing the 3HO lifestyle and Kundalini Yoga as taught by Yogi Bhajan®. For more information about Kundalini Yoga as taught by Yogi Bhajan® please see www.kundaliniresearchinstitute.org.

To the spirit source of inspiration

To all the souls who wish to
heal sexual violence

To my husband
To my family
To those who supported me,
for without you, I would not be here

To survivors and those
going through it

We are the mirror as well as the face in it.
We are tasting the taste this minute
of eternity. We are pain
And what cures pain, both. We are
the sweet cold water and the jar that pours.

Rumi

FOREWORD

Sexual violence is far more common than statistics of crime attest because it remains a taboo in our society and is often not reported. Sadly, treatment and facilities for victims are few and far between. This excellent book could only have been written by a woman with the depth of professional experience of the subject that the author Simranjeet Kaur has had at considerable personal cost.

Her application of Kundalini Yoga and Meditation to address the complexities of Post-Traumatic Stress Disorder in relation to sexual violence is inspired, and does a great service to the medical, social care, and yoga communities. Using the traditions of an ancient healing system therapeutically to heal the emotional and pain bodies, the author empowers her readers to release the pain of past memories, to harmonize their mental state, and reconnect with the impulses of their core psyche.

This is a valuable and eminently practical contribution to healing sexual violence in the twenty-first century.

Guru Dharam Khalsa BAcC RCHM
Director International School of Kundalini Yoga iSKY
June 20th, 2022

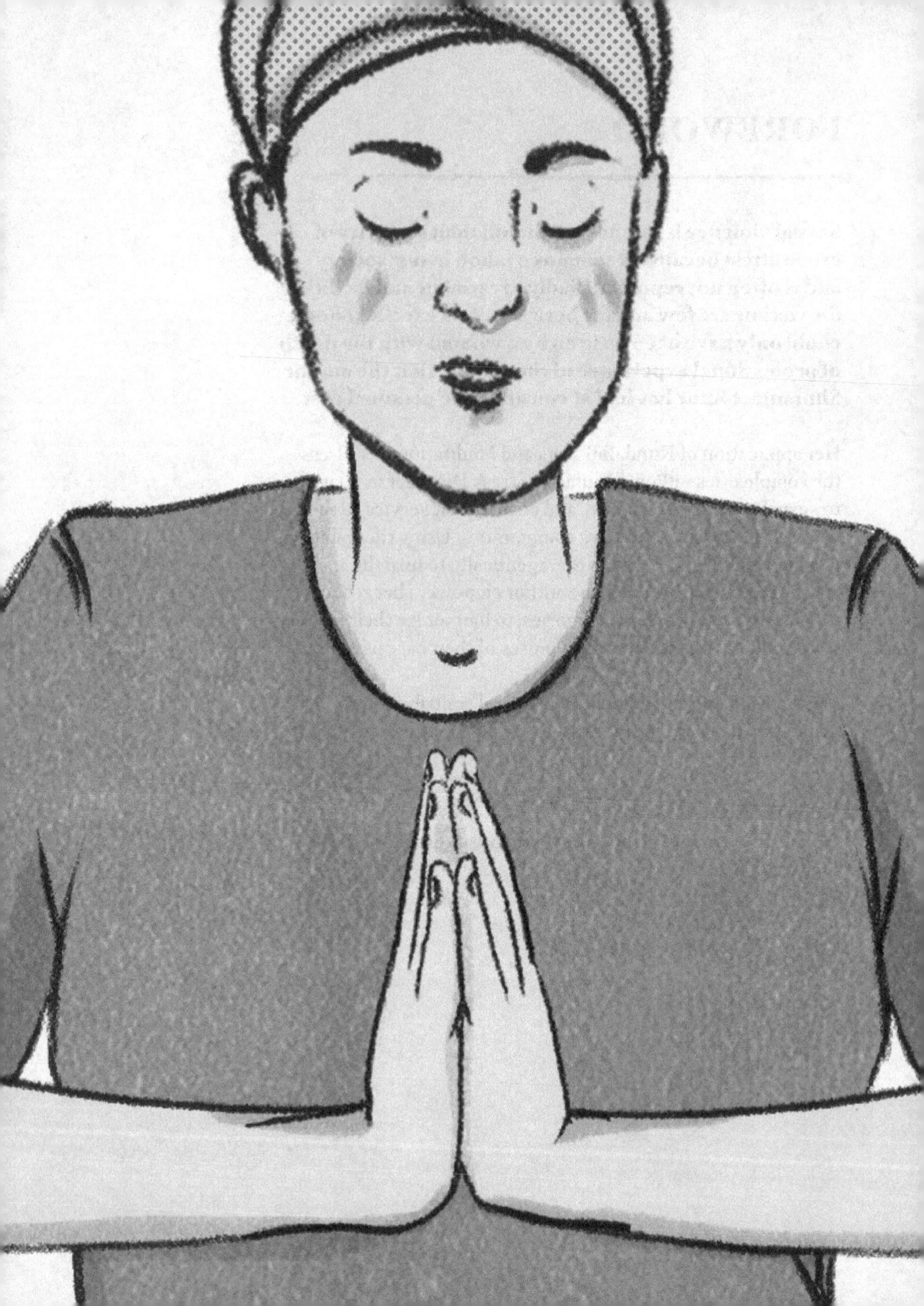

SUMMARY

WELCOMING MESSAGE

Welcome to *Finding Peace within Shattered Pieces – Healing Trauma with Yoga and Meditation.* This is a book about sexual violence and healing through Kundalini Yoga. If you've picked it up, it's likely that this subject is important to you and you want to heal yourself or others. I've created this book to provide ideas, insights and inspiration to help you make your own choices and do the work of healing effectively and compassionately.

Healing is essential. It takes effort and endurance, but it is enriching and a source of immense pleasure. People who have learned to self-heal by drawing on the strength of their inner self are successful, creative beings who forge their way through life and follow their hearts and destinies. When it comes to sexual violence, complete healing is vital so that the wounds and scars don't take over your thoughts, identity and life. Personally I can say that I wholeheartedly want you to heal well.

I divided this book into three sections, each covering one helpful aspect of the healing process. The sections include real-life experiences and related information, such as cases I've worked on and the role of the law in the process. The first section shares key information you need to know if you have suffered or witnessed sexual violence. The second section shares the basic yogic philosophy behind Kundalini Yoga. The third and the most robust section features Kundalini Yoga sets and meditations, which I have selected from five years of personal practice as a foundation for your own 40-day program. By using the meditations and practices consistently over 40 days, change happens.

These tools can give you access to the divine consciousness within you and set you on a steady path to recovery, transformation, and healing. It is my intention to guide you through a journey from within, and I consider this nothing less than your divine and sacred journey that deserves reverence and respect for yourself and others. This program can help you build a life you can love and be proud of — and have lots of joy practicing it along the way. I know that this kind of experience can give you the trust and desire to continue with this journey on your own.

SAYING NO TO TRAUMA AND CHRONIC STRESS

All of life is communication. Everything we do is also communication with the universe, just as everything that happens in our lives is a way for the universe to communicate back to us. One message I received from my own life experience is: Life is always precious in all its forms, and there is a divine purpose behind everything that happens, even when we face the trauma of sexual violence. This message became my belief and the foundation of my healing. It helped me come to terms with the trauma and the secondary traumatic stress[1] I suffered myself from my former work as a detective for sexual violence crimes.

As a Police Officer, I have seen the worst side of humanity. I have been spat at and routinely abused physically and verbally. Some of the abuse was directed towards me and my family. I have dealt with seriously sexually abused children, the bloody mangled bodies of fatal road traffic accidents, the bruised and battered victims of racism, homophobia and domestic violence, parents cradling dead children, murder victims, people driven to suicide and self-harm. Throughout 30 years on duty, I have recovered numerous dead bodies with dignity, so families could find peace at the return of a loved one. Day after day, I witnessed horrific scenes that luckily the majority of the population only read about. I have saved lives and I have also watched life slip away.

1. ACCORDING TO SPECIALISTS OSOFSKY, PUTNAM & LEDERMAN (2008), SECONDARY TRAUMATIC STRESS IS A SET OF OBSERVABLE REACTIONS TO WORKING WITH PEOPLE WHO HAVE BEEN TRAUMATIZED, AND IT MIRRORS THE SYMPTOMS OF POST-TRAUMATIC STRESS DISORDER (PTSD). PHYSICIANS, PSYCHOTHERAPISTS, HUMAN SERVICE WORKERS AND EMERGENCY WORKERS ARE SOME EXAMPLES OF PROFESSIONALS THAT ARE VULNERABLE TO DEVELOPING THIS TYPE OF STRESS BECAUSE THEY ARE OFTEN EXPOSED ON A DAILY BASIS TO TRAUMATIC AND TROUBLING EVENTS: EITHER TO PEOPLE WHO HAVE BEEN TRAUMATIZED THEMSELVES, DISTURBING DESCRIPTIONS OF TRAUMATIC EVENTS BY A SURVIVOR, OR OTHERS INFLICTING CRUELTY ON ONE ANOTHER. THE SYMPTOMS MAY INCLUDE FEELINGS OF ISOLATION, ANXIETY, DISSOCIATION, PHYSICAL AILMENTS, AND SLEEP DISTURBANCES. THE NATIONAL CHILD TRAUMATIC STRESS NETWORK QUALIFIES IT AS AN INDIRECT TRAUMA EXPOSURE, AND EXPLAINS THAT "FOR THERAPISTS, CHILD WELFARE WORKERS, CASE MANAGERS, AND OTHER HELPING PROFESSIONALS INVOLVED IN THE CARE OF TRAUMATIZED CHILDREN AND THEIR FAMILIES, THE ESSENTIAL ACT OF LISTENING TO TRAUMA STORIES MAY TAKE AN EMOTIONAL TOLL THAT COMPROMISES PROFESSIONAL FUNCTIONING AND DIMINISHES QUALITY OF LIFE".

Sexual violence is a serious offence. It is a crime under the purview of international legal instruments[2] . I have seen how it hurts people and inflicts unbearable wounds. I believe it is a common human responsibility to recognise abuse when we observe it and take action, so that we can all live in a safe environment. This is also the official responsibility of the police, to respond to sexual violence in the community, to assess the circumstances, to support and comfort the victims, apprehend the offenders, and to liaise with support services and take the case to the judicial system. And yet, this doesn't always happen.

Sexual assault affects millions of people worldwide every year. According to data from the United Kingdom's Office of National Statistics, 183,587 people reported sexual violence to police in the year ending in December 2021, a 22% rise over the same period in 2020[3]. Rape accounted for 37% of these cases. According to the US Rape, Abuse, and Incest National Network, an estimated 463,634 people are victims of rape and sexual assault in the United States each year[4]. This means that every 68 seconds an American is sexually assaulted. During the two weeks following a rape, 94% of women exhibit symptoms of post-traumatic stress disorder (PTSD). Nine months after being raped, 30% of women suffer from PTSD symptoms. Work, school, or family/ friends problems affect 38% of victims of sexual abuse[5].

The effects of trauma vary in intensity and combination. They express themselves in ongoing difficulties, often masked with depression, grief, anger, withdrawal, and eventually gripping and grasping at life. Symptoms may first appear physically, in the digestive system or mentally with a shift in mood — no longer the joyful, happy, social self. Emotions flare up suddenly and intensely for no apparent reason. Foremost, trauma effects can get into the nervous system, which can become compounded with fight or flight emotions, manifesting in anger outbursts,

2. ALTHOUGH MANY PARTS OF THE WORLD DON'T HAVE ENFORCEMENT MECHANISM THAT STRONGLY PROHIBITS SEXUAL VIOLENCE, THERE IS A COLLECTION OF INTERNATIONAL LEGAL INSTRUMENTS, SUCH AS TREATIES, CONVENTIONS, PROTOCOLS, DECLARATIONS, RESOLUTIONS AND RECOMMENDATIONS, DEVELOPED IN THE 20TH AND 21ST CENTURY WITH THE AIM TO ADDRESS THE PROBLEM OF SEXUAL VIOLENCE AND PREVENT IT FROM BEING COMMITTED WHEREVER POSSIBLE. ACTS OF SEXUAL VIOLENCE CAN BE CHARGED AS A CRIME AGAINST HUMANITY, GENOCIDE, A WAR CRIME, OR A GRAVE BREACH OF THE GENEVA CONVENTIONS. [EDITOR'S NOTE]

3. "CRIME IN ENGLAND AND WALES: YEAR ENDING DECEMBER 2021", A REPORT FROM THE UK OFFICE FOR NATIONAL STATICS, 28 APRIL 2022, AT HTTPS://WWW.ONS.GOV.UK/PEOPLEPOPULATIONANDCOMMUNITY/CRIMEANDJUSTICE/BULLETINS/CRIMEINENGLANDANDWALES/YEARENDINGDECEMBER2021. ACCESSED JUNE 10, 2022.

4. SEE DEPARTMENT OF JUSTICE, OFFICE OF JUSTICE PROGRAMS, BUREAU OF JUSTICE STATISTICS, NATIONAL CRIME VICTIMIZATION SURVEY, 2019 (2020).

5. SEE "VICTIMS OF SEXUAL VIOLENCE: STATISTICS", AT HTTPS://WWW.RAINN.ORG/STATISTICS/VICTIMS-SEXUAL-VIOLENCE. ACCESSED JUNE 10, 2022.

moments of intense crying, hyper-vigilance, acute sensory perception and extreme reactions to small sensations in the environment. It can also affect the nerve endings in the brain and the ability to process information. These reactions are also very common in war veterans, victims of other violent crimes, and PTSD sufferers. A common reaction in all victims in order to reduce the chance of fear and pain is to engage in avoidance patterns, such as restricting movements and exposure to situations that stir up memories and feelings.

When we are traumatized, we flinch. We close down instead of opening up. This creates a spiral of never-ending action and reaction, moving between fear, blame and revenge, and/or depression, grief, and withdrawal. Each trauma that lies unprocessed forms a kind of an exoskeleton, protecting us from the things we fear. The story of trauma is often seated so firmly in our bodies and our subconscious that those experiences become the foundation of our beliefs, wiring themselves into the fiber of our muscles, organs and nervous system. Our body holds onto that initial reaction and continues to restrict us in subtle ways. We begin to manage our emotions based on fear as if preparing for the next disaster.

We need ways to access our own interior spaces and authenticity so that we can access the trauma, acknowledge it and begin to heal — responding to the world with openness and receptivity. The more we can reduce stress, the easier it is to open up and connect to the realm of spirit, of infinite possibility, connect to our intuition and feel expansion. We can embrace the world again, manage our emotions consciously, and move towards a life built on kindness and generosity. That is a wonderful power and a true strength. Yoga and meditation can create a kind of breakthrough by creating space for the mind to clear out the darkness, become quiet, and return to a sense of safety and security within oneself. Yoga and meditation also help with the one thing you are in complete control of — your relationship with yourself. That brings a certain simplicity to the healing process even when the story of the trauma seems complex.

Throughout my career, I have always asked questions like: Why am I seeing the things I see and why does humanity harm itself the way it does? These inquiries took me on a journey of self-discovery and invited me to remember a concept that has been with me since my earliest beginnings: the concept of divine consciousness. My duty often brought it to the forefront of my mind.

From a spiritual perspective, it is said that suffering is caused by ignorance, and I suffered from ignorance because I didn't always see the divine consciousness in what was in front of me. By connecting to this consciousness or soul, I could free myself from suffering. In this process of healing my wounds, there was a stage where I could find the lesson and acknowledge that I am whole, and that – although this is not the way I would write the script to become whole – it is what was given to me to experience. In that stage, I found that I love myself for who I am, with all my life experiences. What I am describing is a surrender to spiritual knowledge — the knowledge that spirit runs through all things, through all living beings, and knows exactly what it is doing. This of course does not relieve the perpetrator of their responsibility for causing harm, but it allowed me (and it can allow you) to transform from victim to victor.

By embracing this inherent perfection in all aspects of my life, I was able to come to terms with my own trauma. It is my personal belief that we live in a world of divine truth and consciousness, that spirit flows through everything: it is indiscriminate and loves unconditionally. I believe our souls are born into the human experience, and as humans, we must respond in the most humane way. I know that's easier said than done, and the reality can seem quite different, especially when we face trauma, sexual violence, sexual harrassment or domestic abuse.

This is where Kundalini Yoga comes in, where Kundalini Yoga found me. It is a technology for building the bridge for you, from the concept of divine consciousness being everywhere to the lived reality of it. That's exactly what the practice of yoga and meditation has done for me. It opened me and allowed me to go deeper into a union with what I understand to be divine consciousness. It has shown me an inner strength and guidance system and gently restored a sense of balance. In the process, it has transformed everything I have experienced and enabled me to love everything just the way it is.

In this sense, the experience of union that my yoga practice has given me has released the effects of trauma and suffering. In a world that seems unkind, it has connected me with unique individuals who support me in this understanding of unity. So it is perhaps not by chance that I now teach about Kundalini Yoga and sexual violence, so that I can do the same for others.

HOW THIS PROGRAM WILL HELP YOU

The benefits of this program are many and varied. You will learn about legal issues, so you can make informed decisions in the real world about where to turn in cases of sexual violence. You will also learn how to create daily habits to serve you and to create growth, health, and happiness. At the heart of these new habits are the Kundalini Yoga kriyas and meditations that free the kundalini energy within your body, the energy of consciousness, to release rigid patterns in the muscles and optimize blood flow.

Additionally, with Kundalini Yoga, the parasympathetic nervous system relaxes, which is essential for physical and mental well-being, so that you will be able to center yourself emotionally and achieve a new sense of self from which the divine consciousness can rise. Your life begins to flow, and you become radiant in ways that are visible not only to you but also to everyone else.

You can choose to practice the 40 kriyas in the sequence that we present here as a healing program. You can also choose the kriyas and meditations according to your preferences and particular needs, as well as your physiology and psyche, to allow wisdom to expand on all levels of your existence. We are all unique, and the program honors that. Another way of approaching this collection of kriyas and meditations is to pick one at a time and practice it for however many days you feel like you want to. You can also experiment with a new sequence of kriyas and meditations.

As you enter into a process of healing layers of trauma, know that each person has their own experience and pace — with their own memories and triggers. For one person, they may smoothly go through the program day by day; for another, they may have memories or somatic experiences that may call for going slowly, pausing altogether, or staying with one step until they feel ready. And as with any healing program, you should also gather your own resources: a dear friend, a therapist or healer you can talk to about how your process is going, especially if you hit a roadblock or trigger point.

Sometimes it can feel like a rug has been pulled out from under your feet, and it's easy to fall into a pit of darkness and despair. When you are ready, let's begin to build a solid new foundation: to heal step by step, day by day, commit to ourselves, and step into an upward spiral so we can evolve and discover the innocence of our souls. As the great 13th century Sufi philosopher Rumi once wrote, "Let yourself be silently drawn by the strange pull of what you really love. It will not lead you astray."

This book is my promise of healing to you, to the world, to spirit.

Blessings,
Simranjeet

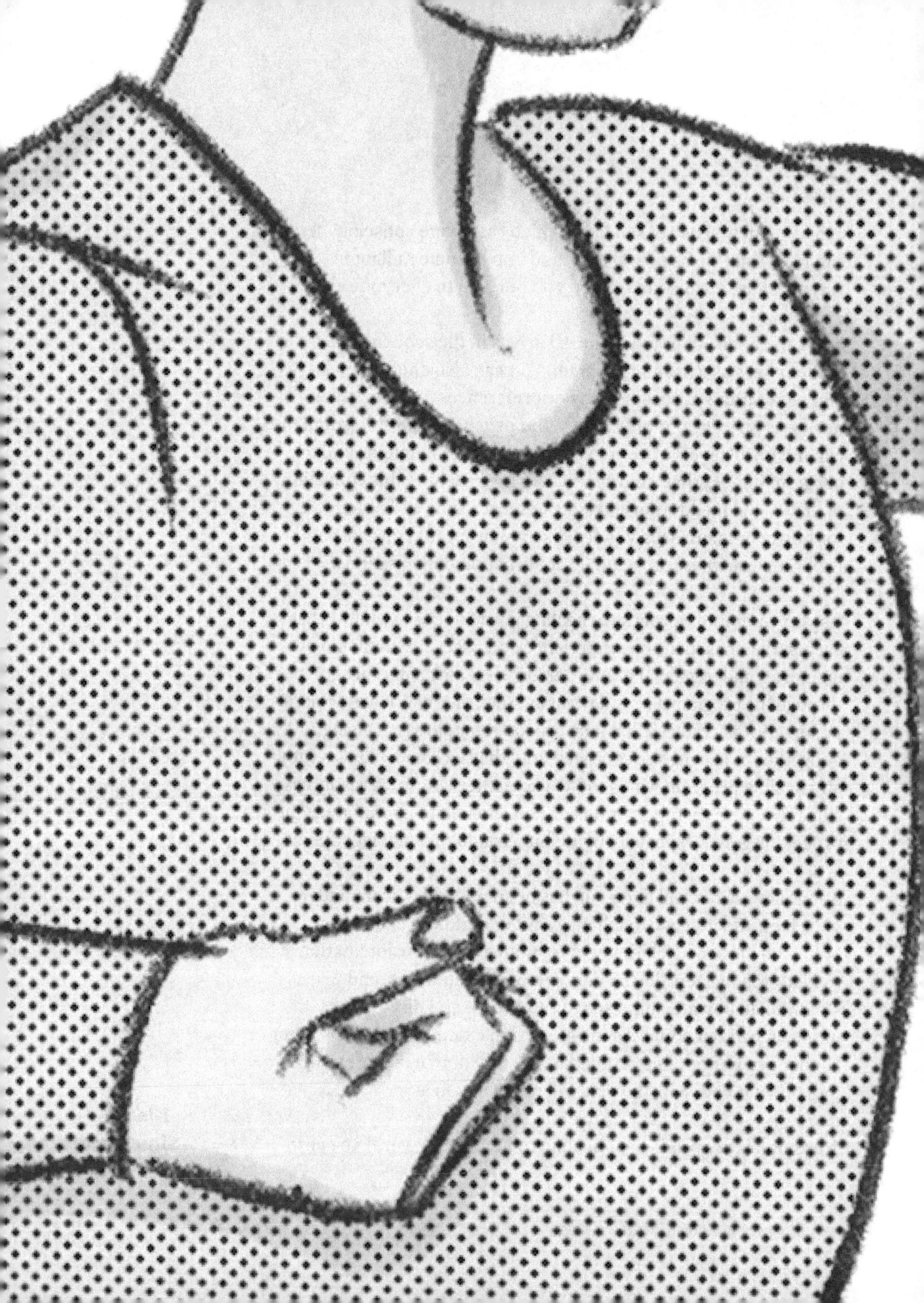

CHAPTER 1.
BREAKING THE MYTHS

Let us explore several aspects of sexual violence that are often not known or misunderstood. Rape is one of the most serious crimes of sexual violence; it has devastating and long-lasting effects on women and men. At the same time, rape is one of the most misunderstood crimes. One reason is that victims rarely show easily identifiable signs of injury on the outside. Very often, the injuries are internal and include shame, guilt, self-blame and self-loathing, which can make the victim shut down and stay silent with a compulsion to carry on as if everything is normal. This is a common response to sexual trauma and often goes on for weeks, months, or even years until the victim finds the strength to report the crime. Many survivors of sexual violence never do.

Even when women and men choose to speak to the police or to friends, whether it is soon or long after the crime, they often provide inconsistent accounts of what happened because they are held back by strong emotions such as fear, trauma, embarrassment, and genuine horror. When communication is obscured like that, others often assume that the victim is being dishonest.

People who have experienced sexual violence sometimes open up in the presence of a counselor, therapist, or yoga teacher. When that happens, it is essential for their healing that we believe them.

We often think that rape is typically committed by strangers, but the opposite is true. Most rape crimes are committed by someone the victim knew, commonly by a current or former spouse or partner, or by a friend, family member or acquaintance. Rape occurs in all communities, and both victims and perpetrators come from every socioeconomic background. However, different circumstances can affect the degree of trauma, and they include those mentioned above as well as mental health issues, learning disabilities, and previous sexual abuse.

MY LAST CASE

"Guv'nor, we have an allegation," said my detective sergeant, standing in the doorway of my office, "a thirteen-year-old boy is alleging he has been raped."

"What?" "When?" I inquired. I listened to the allegation. A male suspect approached the youngster armed with a knife while he was strolling down the street.

"Four o'clock in the afternoon, guv'nor. He demanded the boy's mobile phone. He led him off the street and into an estate. Up the stairs to a block of flats. On the open landing, he raped him. He told him that's what you get for not having your mobile with you."

The young boy could describe the suspect well, down to the look of the jacket, underwear, and necklace the suspect was wearing. The details were so vivid and unusual that initially I suspected the victim had made the whole thing up. My detective sergeant was asking the same question.

"Well, one way or another, we are going to find out," I said. I deployed a team of detectives. We worked tirelessly around the clock. Within 48 hours, we had forensic evidence and identified a suspect. He was fourteen years old.

My heart sank. "A fourteen-year-old boy. A child accused of raping another child. God help us. What world are we living in?" I sat in the office, closed the door and cried, sobbing at what we were facing. I sobbed through my out-and-out tiredness. My head was spinning and my stomach swollen as I tried to comprehend what all this meant for the boy, his family, the community, and how we could serve justice to all. Could we rehabilitate the offender who had his whole life ahead of him? I tried to keep a straight face so my team wouldn't see the devastation I felt.

The rape of a boy is no less shocking than the rape of a girl. I had already dealt with many deaths, suicides, murders, and rapes as a senior investigating officer, including at least ninety other cases, with perpetrators from all levels of society. But I had never dealt with a situation where the perpetrator was a child, and this troubled me more. Maybe because I am a mother, and this case reminded me of my own children.

"I went directly into the bath," the youngster recalled about the time he was raped. "I warned my brother to stay away. I felt dirty." These words echoed in my mind. They had become familiar from seeing many times how shame, guilt, and self-loathing strip away a person's innocence. After a relentless series of dark tales over 28 years, I had reached the tipping point. This was the end for me, my last case.

Although I was remembering that saying of Yogi Bhajan: "If you can't see God in all, you can't see God at all", at that point, I could not see any light. Our team had stood for truth, criminal justice was served, and the perpetrator was convicted and sentenced to prison. But when the evidence was revealed in the courtroom, it was harrowing. Families were destroyed, and I could only imagine the pain the boy's mother felt. She made a statement about how the rape had changed not only her son's life but the whole family's. It was read out in court and reported in the newspapers: "My son used to be a lively boy but became shy and withdrawn. It breaks my heart."

The judge in the case was Roger Chapple, and as he sentenced the defendant, he told him his offenses were dreadful and the effects on his victim were profound. I am grateful the victim came from a caring family and had a brother who knew him well enough to know something was wrong. If his brother had not paid attention, the crime may have not been reported for many years, or maybe never at all. We can't say for sure, and many others might have become victims of the young perpetrator. What I can say is that the police will serve and protect you and others if you come forward as quickly as possible.

SEXUAL VIOLENCE

There are various aspects to identifying behaviour as sexual violence, and I will discuss them here.

Sexual violence exists on a spectrum of severity, and the various degrees range from sexual assault to rape and attempted rape. These can be names for penetration crimes, i.e., criminal conduct in which one body part penetrates another — a penis or an object penetrating a mouth, anus, or vagina. Sexual assault can also include contact with intimate body parts like genitalia, breasts, buttocks, or the exposure of these parts. All of this behavior can constitute a crime, and there are laws against it. But first, such behaviors must be recognized as a crime, and you may be faced with identifying it and then deciding what to do next.

Consent is another important aspect of identifying sexual violence. Consent is a broad term for various mind-states in sexual activity between individuals, ranging from genuine desire on one end, to reluctant acquiescence on the other.

A crucial question is whether a person had a choice to engage in the particular sexual activity, and whether that choice was unobstructed or influenced. For example, the existence of choice is questionable when a person is asleep, unconscious, or under the influence of drugs or alcohol. Further questions to ask of the other person(s) and yourself in the assessment of any situation as sexual violence can include: Are you able to say no?

Everyone reacts differently to sexual violence, and it is not always easy to understand its effects on an individual. As I mentioned above, some victims will tell no one or wait years before coming forward. Some victims block the event and don't remember it for a period of time. When they speak out, it is vital for true healing that they feel heard and believed in and that others recognize their pain. It doesn't matter who inflicted the harm and injury on them, whether it was a stranger or someone they know, a family member, or an attack by a group, or anyone holding a position of trust in society, such as politicians, teachers or spiritual leaders. Sexual violence happens everywhere, and believing the victim is always key.

People can face many internal barriers when reporting sexual violence. For example, going to the police is not just hard for women. Sometimes it is even harder for men, because the terminology of sexual violence often implies violence against women. That makes it hard for men to relate to the justice system and trust that their needs will be met. In fact, the way men report rape differs from the reporting behaviour of women. Men who are victims of sexual violence are more likely to present the issue as a health problem and seek help at a hospital emergency room or sexual health clinic instead of to the police. Only a shocking third of all assaulted men report to the police, and usually only after at least five years have passed since the incident.

This resistance in men to seeking proper help is compounded when symptoms of Post-Traumatic Stress Disorder (PTSD) enter the mix, especially feelings of shame and guilt. One explanation is the conditioning of males in our society. Males are told from childhood on they must be powerful protectors, and male victims of sexual violence often think they failed, because they can't even protect themselves. When we consider that reporting such a situation to the police often involves facing another man – for instance, a police officer who represents the ultimate strong alpha masculine – we may find it easy to understand why male victims don't come forward.

THE WOUNDED HEALER

Talking to someone about your experience of sexual violence can be one of the biggest challenges, as fear is one of the most common emotions in such a situation. Please remember this first: You don't have to go it alone, but it is important that you seek help as soon as possible. Support has never been more accessible, as awareness about sexual violence is growing quickly, and relevant information is more available now than ever, especially online.

There are many professionals who will help you, including the police and medical workers. As a former police officer, I am always going to direct you to the police first, simply because it is their role and public duty to investigate and serve the victims and the community. They have specialty departments, such as Rape Crisis National Service Standards and Sexual Assault Referral Centres[6], which are services for victims of rape and sexual assault. These agencies aim to be a one-stop service providing sexual health services, medical care, and forensic examination.

6. SIMRANJEET KAUR IS A BRITISH FORMER POLICE OFFICER. HERE SHE IS REFERRING TO AGENCIES AND ENTITIES IN HER HOMELAND. A QUICK SEARCH ON THE INTERNET CAN HELP YOU FIND SIMILAR SERVICES AND ENTITIES IN YOUR COUNTRY AND CITY. REFER TO THE RESOURCE PAGE TO FIND OUT MORE ABOUT NATIONAL ENTITIES IN THE US. [EDITOR'S NOTE]

In addition, you can rely on health professionals such as psychologists and mental health practitioners. A professional will help you understand that rape and sexual abuse can happen to anyone, and what you are going through is normal; so you can stay positive, make the right decisions, and have the chance to bounce back. It can be incredibly reassuring and empowering to just have someone listen to you and give you advice. The good news is that on the other side of adversity is a stronger, wiser, more resilient you.

Just as it is hard for you, it is hard for others. If someone tells you they are the victim of sexual violence, believe them first. Please remember that confiding in someone may be an enormous and daunting step for them, and all survivors deserve the best response, whether or not they report to the police.

Sometimes the fear of reporting a crime is connected to the real or perceived power or status of the person who committed the crime. Don't forget that no one is above the law, no matter how big and powerful you (or they) might think they are. The law is there to preserve life, so please make use of it. I echo the words of Dame Elish, a Scottish lawyer, Scotland's former Lord Advocate and current principal of St Hugh's College, Oxford, who headed a 2015 review of how the police and prosecuting services investigate and prosecute rape cases:

> *We need to look at rape complainants as people who have been harmed, whom society has a positive responsibility to help and to protect, aside from the operations of criminal law. Whether the rape is reported or not, whether or not the case goes forward, whether there is a conviction or not, complainants still have a right to services that will help them to recover and rebuild their*

lives. Complainants and those who work with them have said that the criminal process is important, but getting support and being believed is as important[7].

7. SEE "REPORT OF THE INDEPENDENT REVIEW INTO THE INVESTIGATION AND PROSECUTION OF RAPE IN LONDON", BY RT HON DAME ELISH ANGIOLINI, DBE QC, FROM 30 APRIL 2015, PUBLISHED ON HTTPS://WWW.CPS.GOV.UK/PUBLICATION/REPORT-INDEPENDENT-REVIEW-INVESTIGATION-AND-PROSECUTION-RAPE-LONDON-RT-HON-DAME-ELISH. ACCESSED JUNE 10, 2022.

While living with the consequences of sexual violence can be devastating, it is important to know that, if you seek professional help, it often gets easier, emotional problems can end, and people can successfully reconcile the past with the present to live harmonious, happy lives.

Earlier in this book, I talked about the power of self-healing, and I have found that one key to understanding this human power lies in the archetype of the wounded healer. We are all wounded healers, whether or not we know it. The wounded healer teaches us that our power lies in our wounds, in the sense that it is the wound in me that evokes the healing in you and the wound in you that evokes the healing in me. When we keep our wounds totally private, we separate from this power of connection and deny healing for ourselves and others. Keeping a stiff upper lip is just a way to live without connection and love. Once we share our deepest wounds with the world – whether it is with sexual violence or any other form of hurt – we not only bring the event out into the open, but we also open our hearts and heal ourselves and inspire others to heal themselves.

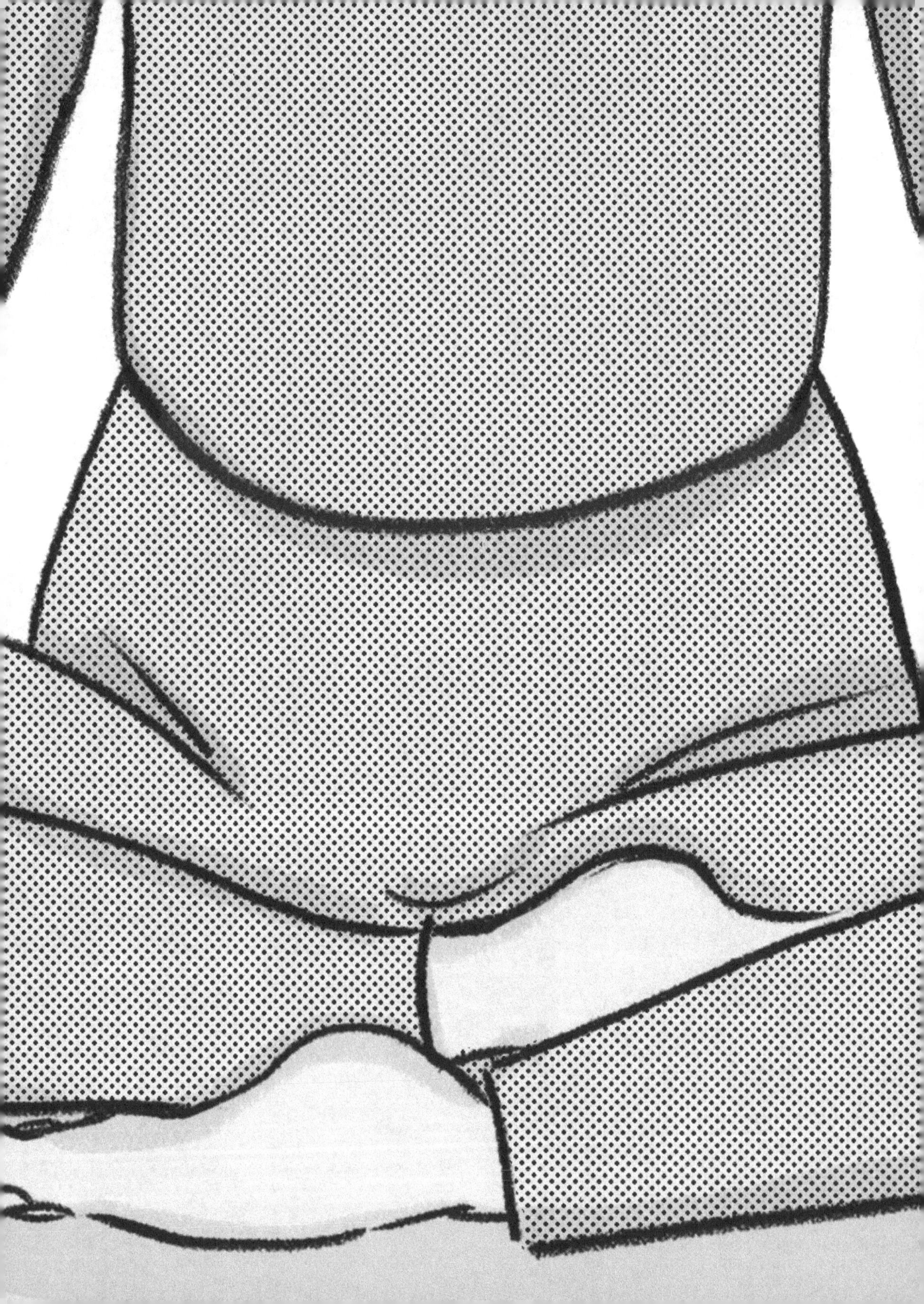

CHAPTER 2.
WHAT IS KUNDALINI YOGA?

These days, yoga is everywhere — because it works. Medical professionals, like doctors and psychologists, as well as scientific research,[8] are increasingly recognizing the beneficial effects it has on recovery and general mental and physical well-being.

8. PLEASE VISIT THE KRI RESEARCH PAGE TO FIND OUT MORE ABOUT THE VARIOUS SCIENTIFICALLY RESEARCHED BENEFITS OF KUNDALINI YOGA. HTTPS://KUNDALINIRESEARCHINSTITUTE.ORG/YOGA-RESEARCH/

Yoga is a spiritual practice that goes back over 3,500 years to the Indus Valley Civilization. Its origins stretch from these early pre-modern hints of yoga to the enlightened people of the Vedic times (1500-500 BCE), also called Rishis. They recorded their findings of meditation, philosophy, and spiritual knowledge in ancient Sanskrit texts; some of the oldest scriptures of Hinduism come from this time, and this includes the Upanishads and Vedas. The focus of the Upanishads is on four primary spiritual themes. The first and most important is the realization that there is no separation between the individual and the universe, or God — that they are the same. The scriptures refer to the universe as the ultimate formless and inconceivable Godhead (Brahman), and the individual part of that, the soul, as Atman.

The word kundalini refers to a particular energy as part of the human circulatory system, and the kundalini energy lies within every human being. It is also called the energy of consciousness, but it is dormant in most humans. Kundalini Yoga is a technology to awaken this energy and to awaken a person's consciousness. Awakening the kundalini energy isn't, of course, exclusive to Kundalini Yoga. You will find references to this process in many cultures and spiritual practices, and each culture has developed its way of waking up this energy. In this book, I am focusing on Kundalini Yoga techniques because these are the practices in which I initiated myself, and with which I went through my own healing journey.

Kundalini Yoga was brought from India to the West by Yogi Bhajan. His declared mission was to create yoga teachers, not to collect students, and to help them become conscious and aware — "to deliver them to the infinite," as he called it. Yogi Bhajan taught Kundalini Yoga as a highly personalized practice and included the practice of mantras, primarily from the Sikh tradition. It is important to note, however, that you do not have to be Sikh or believe in God to practice and benefit from Kundalini Yoga. All you have to do is take part, and the practice will take you where you need to go.

How does the Kundalini Yoga practice support healing processes? As I mentioned before, kundalini is an astonishing energy, which lies usually dormant at the base of the spine until activated. The energy is associated with the divine feminine, called Shakti. Kundalini Yoga uses several techniques to awaken the energy, including yoga postures and movements, breathing techniques, as well as mantra and chanting. These techniques increase the praana, or a life force energy. An increase in praana can help you transcend negative patterns or life experiences. In yogic science, praana is the animating force that permeates everything. From this perspective, it makes sense to look at praana as a controlling factor in life that is stronger than genes. You can think of your mental activity as praana flowing through the body like a water system. Praana supports everything we do in Kundalini Yoga and helps us unite the physical, mental, and spiritual aspects of a human being, even the soul.

It is said that the awakened energy of kundalini travels upward through energy pathways, called nadis, and through specific psychic centers along the spine, called chakras. These chakras are associated with nearby organs and glands. For example, the sixth chakra, which is between the eyebrows at the root of the nose, is associated with the pituitary and pineal glands, which are in the brain behind the eyes. Kundalini energy moves from the chakra at the bottom of the spine, the root chakra, to the chakra at the crown of the head and awakens human consciousness. As it moves higher to the level of pure soul, or divine consciousness, it also brings healing to the person. As soul consciousness manifests through the chakras in the head, the life force, or more simply, the energy of love flows into the heart center, which works as a power station, affecting other chakras and lighting up everything else.

We may feel an awakening in different ways, such as an emotional release with spontaneous laughter or tears, waves of energy moving through the body, or new insights. These experiences are all normal reactions, and they simply mean that something is being worked out. It is not important to know exactly how things are being worked out, but it is helpful to trust the healing power of Kundalini Yoga and the guidance of the universe, to which we are all connected. The healing from these experiences can differ from the results of other modalities, like talk therapy or pharmaceuticals, but it's important to note that all these approaches are complementary to each other. With the practice of Kundalini Yoga in my daily life, associated with other therapies such as acupuncture, herbal medicine and journaling, I have found the healing to be fast and effective, and both challenging and rewarding.

The main reason for the effectiveness of Kundalini Yoga is the focused application of healing power through the specific sets we practice. The sets are called kriyas, and we teach and practice them as Yogi Bhajan gave them to his students. To maintain the optimum effectiveness and integrity of the practice, we don't alter kriyas. At the same time, participation in the practice is a personal relationship, and it can lead to growth, bliss, and freedom from suffering. As Yogi Bhajan often said, "if you do not go within, you go without".

An essential yogic teaching is that anything you seek you can find inside of you. Understanding this basic truth builds confidence and consciousness and is the foundation for a strong internal relationship with yourself. It can take time, practice, and commitment to understand and build this inner foundation. But once you start and keep up, you can lean on your consciousness as something solid — and Kundalini Yoga prepares the body for such a strong spiritual core. But you have to initiate the practice yourself. Sometimes it is trauma that opens the desire that has been building from within, and this can also cause the greatest healing and transformation. As with any healing or energy work, your intention means everything, and how we choose to live determines our life experience.

Sometimes emotions get stuck or erupt without explanation, and we have a difficult time moving on from them. But it is important to remember that everything changes eventually, and according to yogic philosophy, a person changes every 72 hours. If you sit and meditate and let the blood flow through any area of discomfort and disease for a while, you can feel alright, even if it is just by becoming calm through meditation and mindfulness.

When you have a strong connection to your own spirit, you can allow your emotions to be what they are with less reactivity. You can consciously process all the powerful ups and downs of your emotions because you are less identified with them. They become experiences — not who you are. It is so much easier to work through your anger issue when you can honestly feel, "I am experiencing a lot of anger right now," instead of your usual, "I am angry!" This subtle shift of perspective seems small, but is actually a huge step in the healing journey. And a spiritual practice will help you make this shift, by connecting you to a different part of you — your spirit.

WE DO THE WORK

We rarely meet life directly. Sometimes, when things become overwhelming, we turn to ways that attract our attention, relieve our anxiety, and distract us from the pain of the experience. This is one of the reasons for addictions such as smoking, alcohol, gambling, shopping, food, sugar, and others. But distraction only goes so far. If our goal is the transformation from pain to joy, we not only have to experience our emotions fully, but also love where we are. Through our practice, we allow ourselves to experience a situation by sitting with it in full awareness of our emotions. However, when we are fully present like that, we don't have to experience the pain of what we are feeling: whether it be anger, shame, hate, fear, frustration, sadness, loneliness, or unworthiness. Instead of letting these emotions become toxic beliefs that hinder us, we can transform them with the light of our consciousness. After we acknowledge the pain, it is easier to let it go. It can be very challenging to work with these emotions as they arise, but the yoga sets are designed to support the transformation of emotions in a manageable fashion.

It is understandable that you experience emotions like anxiety and fear. These are the most common emotions experienced by those who have been through any trauma. Please never forget that there is no shame in being a survivor of rape or other sexual violence nor have guilt for having developed secondary traumatic stress as I did. You have every right to feel angry. It is important to remember that emotions have virtues; for example, one of the virtues of anger is patience. Patience does not mean to endure, and just grin and bear it. Patience is a way to process the pain or the sadness and learn to love and care for whatever we encounter in life, to be gentle with the healing process, to accept the feelings as they arise, and to have compassion for yourself.

THE POWER OF ACCEPTANCE AND FORGIVENESS

When we begin a spiritual practice like yoga and meditation, we often think we are going to change for the better. This often implies we don't fully accept who and where we are right now, and this non-acceptance is a subtle form of aggression against ourselves. Never forget that, even when you feel angry or off, timid or unworthy, you can still feel love and kindness for yourself.

Kundalini Yoga is not about replacing part of ourselves with something better, nor even denying certain parts of our personality or life experiences. It is about befriending who you already are, and it is the reassurance of your own self. This is the power of acceptance, and a step towards self-forgiveness. When we are able to forgive ourselves for anything and everything, we start building our resilience and compassion, and we come a bit closer to being able to forgive others.

A quick look at the dictionary tells us that the word "to forgive" means "to stop feeling angry or resentful toward somebody who has done something to harm, annoy or upset you; to stop feeling angry with yourself." In its transitive form, that is, to forgive (somebody) something, it means indulgence in the sense "that somebody does not need to pay back money that they have borrowed."[9] In some way, forgiving involves interrupting the duration of a feeling, or letting go and forgetting. But we know that we need intelligent ways and tested methods that help us do all these things. It's not by a command of the mind that we will all of a sudden stop a feeling from recurring or reappearing and, like a magic trick, forgive and forget.

9. OXFORD LEARNER'S DICTIONARY, HTTPS://WWW.OXFORDLEARNERSDICTIONARIES.COM/US/DEFINITION/ENGLISH/FORGIVE?Q=FORGIVE. ACCESSED MAY 10, 2022.

The Jungian analyst Clarissa Pinkola Estés teaches us in the book *Women Who Run With the Wolves* that to truly forgive ourselves we should sit with our rage, even invite it for a tea and talk for a while so that we can find out what brought this visitor. With practice and patience, we understand what practical uses we can receive from our rage, how it can set some things in motion or reinvigorate certain areas of our lives.

Estés helps us understand that we cannot cleanse ourselves of our rage once and for all. It's a constant work that can be done as a periodic cleansing ritual, a ritual that liberates us bit by bit, leaving ashes where initially a fire was burning. The process of forgiveness has many layers and multiple stages. The important aspect of it, as Estés points out, is to begin and persist.

According to Estés, there are four stages of forgiveness. The first is to forgo. It is to leave it alone, remove the pressing presence of the painful issue from our hearts and minds, and allow the issue to drop away for a while. The second is to forbear, to abstain from punishment. It's about not thinking of the subject nor reacting to it. To forbear means cultivating patience and channeling the emotions. The third stage is to forget; to refuse to linger on the matter, to let it go, to put it off. Finally, there is to forgive — to abandon the debt. It is the conclusion of all the foregoing, forbearing, and forgetting.

As Estés writes, "Some choose blanket pardon: releasing a person from any restitution now or ever. Others choose to call a halt to redress in process, abandoning the debt, saying whatever has been done is done, and the payback is now enough. Another kind of pardon is to release a person without his having made any emotional or other sort of restitution. To some, a finalizing of forgiving means to regard the other indulgently, and this is easiest with regard to relatively benign offenses. One of the most profound forms of forgiveness is to give compassionate aid to the offending person in one form or another. This does not mean you should stick your head in the snake's basket, but instead respond from a stance of mercy, security, and preparedness."[10]

10. ESTÉS, CLARISSA PINKOLA. *WOMEN WHO RUN WITH THE WOLVES: MYTHS AND STORIES OF THE WILD WOMAN ARCHETYPE.* NEW YORK: BALLANTINE BOOKS, 1992, P. 272.

The social work researcher and best-selling author Brené Brown reminds us that for forgiveness to take place, something needs to die, and because of that, it's important to live through the loss and grief. In her perspective, forgiveness seems difficult most of the time because it involves death and grief. There is no other way other than facing the pain, sitting with it, processing it and releasing it. "Given the dark fears we feel when we experience loss, nothing is more generous and loving than the willingness to embrace grief in order to forgive," writes Brené Brown in her New York Times bestselling book *Rising Strong*[11].

11. BROWN, BRENÉ. *RISING STRONG: HOW THE ABILITY TO RESET TRANSFORMS THE WAY WE LIVE, LOVE, PARENT, AND LEAD.* NEW YORK: RANDOM HOUSE, 2017, P. 173.

Commenting on a quote from Archbishop Desmond Tutu, Brown remarks that forgiveness is not walking away from accountability or condoning a hurtful act. It's rather a process of naming your experiences, owning your stories, and healing your wounds so you can truly live.

In this framework, Kundalini Yoga can help you to get in touch with your emotions, to sit with them as for a tea, talk to them and hear them without necessarily identifying with them. Yoga practice and meditation can provide you with an opportunity to experience something inside you that is beyond attachment or personal beliefs, something that is pure, compassionate and kind. Through the practice of meditation, you learn to become an observer of your thoughts and to stop them in their tracks if they are not relevant or helpful.

With persistent practice and constant kind contact with your emotions, you can slowly build on the virtue of forgiveness. Forgiveness and mercy comes with time. It will come in a natural way if you allow it to unfold. Forgiveness comes from the heart. It is compassion in a beautiful and natural way. The soul's truth lives in a space of innocence and is free of harm. You can always go there to let the divine consciousness unravel from within — and when you do, take the space and the time to heal. Allow yourself to get deeply in touch with that purity in you that will reveal unimaginable new perspectives of your own self and your soul.

Yogi Bhajan once said that "the process of self-healing is the privilege of every being. Self-healing is a genuine process of the relationship between the physical and the infinite power of the soul."[12]

12. THE LIBRARY OF TEACHINGS, OCTOBER 7TH, 1994. HTTP://LIBRARYOFTEACHINGS.ORG

START WHERE YOU ARE

When we begin a spiritual practice like yoga and meditation, it is easy to get caught up in the mind as it gives us an abundance of reasons to see the practice as irrational. And we don't always understand why we are drawn to some things and not others, and what exactly happens when we engage in something new like Kundalini Yoga. You have probably experienced (as I have) that understanding often comes over time. Many practitioners report that Kundalini Yoga touches their heart and soul.

So when you are practicing Kundalini Yoga, be kind to yourself, accept whatever you think or feel, unapologetically. Practice self-love. Look at it from a different experience, as the divine lovingly removes your old armor because you are simply growing out of it. This is God's love. So let the release happen and allow the tears to flow in acceptance if they come.

Kundalini Yoga, with its rhythmic, unforced, graceful and liberating movements, relaxes the entire body and releases the tensions we store in the body from our daily emotions. Because of that, it is normal if you cry or feel like you want to. If the reaction of your body is to cry, let it happen. When it comes to crying emotional tears, a research study published in 2014 in the journal *Frontiers in Psychology*[13] found that crying has a self-soothing effect on people, because it stimulates the parasympathetic nervous system, which in turn helps people relax. It also releases oxytocin and endorphins, chemicals that make people feel good and ease physical and emotional pain. In this way, crying can help reduce pain and promote well-being.

13. GRAČANIN, A., BYLSMA, L. M., & VINGERHOETS, A. J. (2014). IS CRYING A SELF-SOOTHING BEHAVIOR?. *FRONTIERS IN PSYCHOLOGY, 5*, 502. HTTPS://DOI.ORG/10.3389/FPSYG.2014.00502

One key to the breakthroughs in my healing journey was giving myself permission to relax deeply and signal to my body that it is safe to get on with the healing. I learned to breathe deeply, to accept God's grace, and to allow life to unfold so I could be happy and healthy. You too can release and heal in this way.

LISTEN TO YOUR NEEDS

You reach a point where you ask yourself, "So what do I do to get better?" When I asked myself that question, an inner voice told me to see Guru Dharam Singh Khalsa, a Kundalini Yoga teacher who is also an acupuncturist. It was a leap of faith to book a healing session with him, and I was very nervous before meeting him in the treatment room. He was going to put needles into my body and I didn't want to discuss my experiences or relive memories unnecessarily. Although I never shared a single story with him, I wanted treatment for extreme stress largely incurred through my job with the metropolitan police force. My symptoms mirror Secondary Traumatic Stress (STS) symptoms, such as a pattern of extreme stress caused by incessant and long-standing emotional overload, erratic sleeping patterns, energy problems and feelings of being locked in.

According to Guru Dharam, the emotional overload was locking my liver meridian in extreme stagnation, and the blocking by emotional debris was compounded by continued exposure to horrible sights and cases involving extreme brutality. Additionally, the adrenal glands were overloaded from being in a constant state of high alert, which was consuming my kidney and heart energy, locking the heart chakra. My treatment regime included relaxation of the liver meridian, support for the kidneys and heart healing through acupuncture, Chinese herbal medicine, sound healing and Kundalini Yoga and meditation practices.

I saw Guru Dharam for 45-minute treatment sessions monthly for two years. My progress curve was fairly steady, and I experienced occasional breakthrough releases of memories that had been especially difficult. As my inner strength gradually returned, the healing process gathered momentum. This helped me to make some life-changing decisions.

My treatment inspired me to select the 40 kriyas and meditations that you see in the next section, all of them practiced over a period of 5 years, led by the principle of releasing emotional stagnation without triggering flashbacks, balancing the liver energy, toning of the kidneys and adrenals, and opening the heart. While picking the practices, I also guided myself by themes like releasing fear and removing body blocks, but foremost, balancing the physical, emotional, mental, energetic, and spiritual parts of ourselves, strengthening intuition, developing trust and building self-love.

CHAPTER 3. HEALING TRAUMA 40-DAY PROGRAM

There is something hopeful about beginning a new meditation or yoga practice. It's like starting a new journal. It's a blank page of possibility, an opportunity to reimagine what could be. A promise of a new beginning each day.

Practicing Kundalini Yoga and its wonderful meditations doesn't have to be done all day. It can be as simple as three or eleven minutes. Yet the benefits do last throughout the day. Through mantra, breathing techniques and postures, Kundalini Yoga and meditation is a wonderful opportunity to quiet the mind, observe the emotions, and create the space for the healing process to manifest and unfold. We use these yogic techniques to enter into a relationship with our full range of emotional vitality in the present moment.

Please remember that each day builds on the previous one. A daily practice builds spiritual strength, which gives great resilience. It supports something in you that allows you to go with the flow. This can percolate as a strength when the physical capacity or emotional aspect of the self finds itself weary and drained, and feels helpless in the face of some seemingly insurmountable problem. When the spirit seeks to reassert its need for extra spiritual strength, that's where the effects of a daily Kundalini Yoga practice catapult us forward, towards a better self and a peaceful day-to-day reality.

This 40-day program is an opportunity to explore your inner self. It's also an opportunity to allow your own internal system to guide you. To do that, it's really important to allow yourself the whole experience and not to deny anything you feel as it comes up. This program is just moving the energy that no longer serves you to make space for something new.

Your power to heal is in your feelings. Begin to experience and feel the feelings. If you are practicing within this program and nursing a wound or an old injury, honor that by being kind to yourself. It's not something that needs to be forced. The spirit is gentle and compassionate. Allow the feelings of love and self-love to blossom. The secret is to allow yourself to take your time. Patience and practice are essential tools in any form of spiritual awakening and healing. The most essential piece of equipment is you. Just you, simply you. Nothing but you.

I encourage you to journal throughout your healing process. Take notes each day of how you feel the practice has impacted your day. You may also choose to freely express yourself, just letting the hand flow with your thoughts and feelings. Journalling is a form of self-expression, an opportunity to slow down, observe the inner thought process and enjoy the moment. It offers insights and renewal, whether the writing is intended for anyone else's eyes or not.

Look at this healing journey as an unfolding just like flower buds unfold through the spring and blossom in the summer. The practices become part of life, not a marathon to be done in so many minutes or days.

BEFORE YOU BEGIN

If you're new to Kundalini Yoga, note that it's always a good practice to tune in before you begin your yoga each day. Here we share key points to be aware of when doing the practices below.

TUNING IN

Every Kundalini Yoga session begins with chanting the Adi Mantra, "Ong Namo Guru Dev Namo." By chanting it with the right pronunciation and projection, the student becomes open to their higher self, the source of all guidance, and accesses the protective link between himself or herself and the consciousness of the divine teacher.

Sit in a comfortable cross-legged position with the spine straight. Place the palms of the hands together as if in prayer, with the fingers pointing straight up, and then press the joints of the thumbs into the center of the chest at the sternum. Inhale deeply. Focus your concentration on the Third Eye Point. As you exhale, chant the entire mantra in one breath. If you can't chant on a single breath, then take a quick sip of air through the mouth after "Ong Namo" and then chant the rest of the mantra, extending the sound as long as possible. The sound "Dev" is chanted a minor third higher than the other sounds of the mantra. As you chant, let the sound vibrate the inner chambers of the sinuses and the upper palate to create a mild pressure at the Third Eye Point. The mouth is slightly open and the lips held firm, increasing the resonance while the sound comes out through the nose. Chant this mantra at least three times before beginning your Kundalini Yoga practice.

The "O" sound in Ong is long, as in "go", and of short duration. The "ng" sound is long and produces a definite vibration on the roof of the mouth and the cranium. The "O", as in "go", is held longer. The first syllable of Guru is pronounced as in the word "good." The second syllable rhymes with "true." The first syllable is short and the second one is long. The word Dev rhymes with "gave".

"Ong" is the infinite creative energy experienced in manifestation and activity. It is a variant of the cosmic syllable "Om," which refers to God in Its absolute or unmanifest state. "Namo" has the same root as the Sanskrit word "Namaste", which means reverent greetings. It implies bowing down. Together, "Ong Namo" means "I call on the infinite creative consciousness," and it opens you to the universal consciousness that guides all action.

"Guru" is the embodiment of the wisdom that one is seeking. "Dev" means higher, subtle, or divine. It refers to the spiritual realms. "Namo", at the end of the mantra, reaffirms the humble reverence of the student. Taken together, "Guru Dev Namo" means, "I call on the divine wisdom," whereby you bow before your higher self to guide you in using the knowledge and energy given by the cosmic self.

PACING YOURSELF

Kundalini Yoga exercises may involve rhythmic movement between two or more postures. Begin slowly, keeping a steady rhythm. Then increase gradually, as the body allows, being careful not to strain. Be sure that the spine has become warm and flexible before attempting rapid movements. It is important to be aware of your body and to be responsible for its well-being.

CONCLUDING AN EXERCISE

Unless it says otherwise, an exercise ends by inhaling and holding the breath for a short time, then exhaling and relaxing the posture. While the breath is being held, apply the Root Lock, contracting the muscles around the anal sphincter, the sex organs, and the Navel Point, while drawing the navel back towards the spine. This consolidates the effects of any exercise and circulates the energy to your higher centers. Suspend the breath just beyond a level of comfort. If you experience any discomfort, immediately release the lock and exhale.

WARM-UPS

I have picked three series of exercises for you to practice as warm-ups during the 40-day program. You can practice them at your will and at your own pace. I recommend that you do at least one of the following three sets of exercises every day before you get into the more physical or meditative kriyas.

WARM-UP I

Originally published in The Aquarian Teacher Level 2 — Lifecycles and Lifestyles

1) Sit in Easy Pose with a straight spine and a light Neck Lock. Place your hands in Gyan Mudra on the knees (thumb and index finger together). Begin Breath of Fire and continue for **3 minutes**.

2) Remain in Easy Pose. Extend both arms straight out to the sides, with the palms facing up. Begin Breath of Fire and continue for **3 minutes**.

3) Remain in Easy Pose. Bring the palms together in Prayer Pose at the Heart Center. Begin Breath of Fire and continue for **3 minutes**.
TO END: Inhale deeply and exhale. Repeat **2 more times**. Relax.

WARM-UP II

1) Yoga March. Stand up with the feet hip width apart. Inhale and raise both arms straight up and raise one leg bringing the knee up as high as possible; exhale and bring the arms and leg down. Continue alternating legs for **3 minutes**.

2) Camel Ride. Sit in Easy Pose with a straight spine and a light Neck Lock. Grasp the shins or the ankles with the hands. Tilt the pelvis forward on the inhale, lifting the chest up, and backward on the exhale. Only the pelvis and lower spine move. The rib cage, shoulders and head are still and remain over the hips. The motion is fluid. Continue for **3 minutes** with a powerful breath.

3) Torso Twist. Remain in Easy Pose. Grasp the shoulders with the fingers in front and the thumbs in back, and lift the elbows out to the sides and up to shoulder height. Twist the whole torso to the left on the inhale and to the right on the exhale. Keep the upper arms out to the sides and parallel to the ground. The head moves last. The motion is fluid. Continue for **3 minutes**.

4) Shoulder Shrugs. Remain in Easy Pose. Rest the hands on the knees or thighs. Raise both shoulders up towards the ears on the inhale, drop the shoulders down on the exhale. Move rapidly for **3 minutes**.

5) Ego Eradicator. Remain in Easy Pose. Roll the shoulders down and open the shoulder blades wide. Raise the arms up and straight to 60 degrees. Curl the fingers onto the mounds at the base of the fingers and pull the knuckles back, stretching the palms wide. Draw the thumbs away from the fingers and point them straight up. Keep the neck and shoulder muscles relaxed, and maintain the arms at a 60 degree angle. Close the eyes and focus on the Third Eye Point, while concentrating above the head. Continue for **3 minutes** with Breath of Fire.
TO END: Inhale, suspend the breath, keep the arms straight and touch the tips of the thumbs together over the head. Open and stretch the fingers wide. Exhale and apply Root Lock. Inhale, exhale, release the Root Lock and slowly lower the arms. Relax.

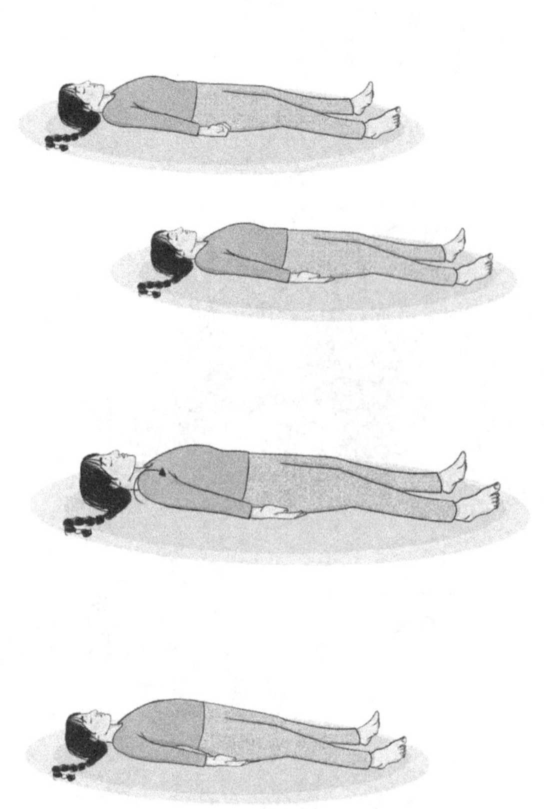

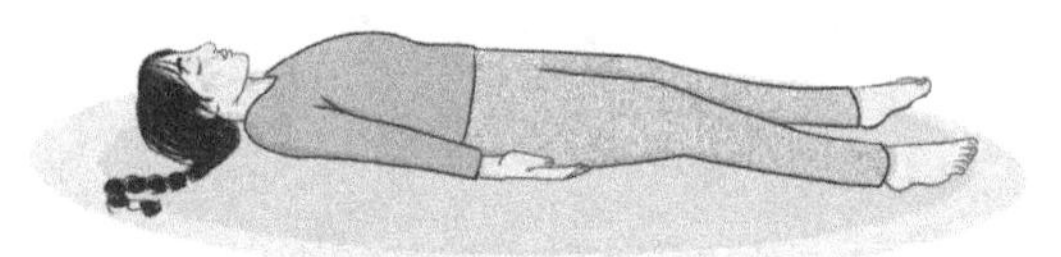

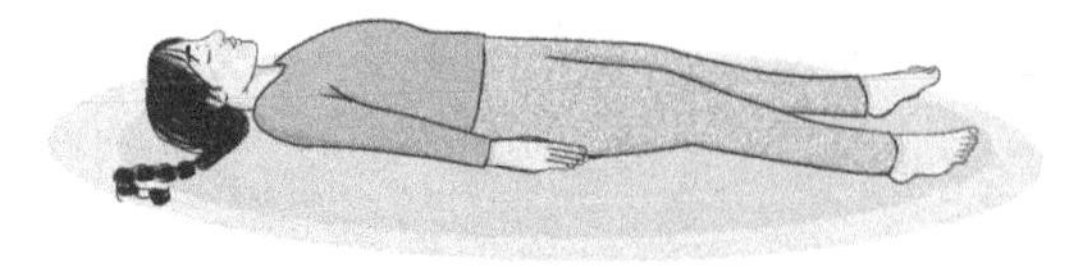

WAKE UP, WARM UP, AND GET UP

Simple Things to Do Before You Get Up in the Morning

March 1992

In the morning, practice the following exercise sequence in bed before opening your eyes and getting up to preserve your health and prevent disease.

1) Clench and release your fingers.

2) Move your shoulders in a circle.

3) Tense and release your lower back.

4) Point your toes.

5) With your hands flat at your sides, stretch your whole body.

6) Curl around sinuously like a snake, moving 3 inches (8 cm) to the left and right.

7) Place the palms of your hands over your eyes, open your eyes while your hands are covering them, and slowly raise your hands away from your eyes. In this way your eyes are gently introduced to the light.

8) Massage your mouth and face with your hands.

9) Cat Stretch. Stretch the arms out to the sides with the palms facing up. Keeping the shoulders and arms on the ground, bend the right knee, take it as far as possible across the body to the left as you turn the head to the right, creating a gentle twist through the spine. The right knee ideally is on the ground to the side of the left knee. Bring the right knee and head back to center, and stretch the right leg straight forward on the ground. Repeat with the left leg.

10) Raise your head up slowly and pull your knees up to your chest.

OPEN THE SPACE IN YOU

We begin this program by aligning and awakening our ten bodies. You will not only move your physical body, but you'll nurture your three mental bodies (the negative, the positive, and the neutral minds) and balance your six energy bodies (soul body, arcline, auric body, praanic body, subtle body and radiant body).

Within every human being there is an energetic circulatory system and the kundalini energy is part of such an energetic system. Kundalini Yoga systemically calls on that energetic system deploying your own power and intelligence within. For that, this particular kriya works on the physical, mental and etheric bodies, through the spinal column and the breath. Consciously breathing on its own brings transformation.

To come to terms with any form of trauma, I invite you to practice this kriya and relate to higher consciousness, by remembering that you are not only your physical body, you are also a spiritual being living a human experience through your other nine bodies. Get to know them, reconnect with them, and let them come into balance through the following kriya.

KRIYA AWAKENING YOUR TEN BODIES

Originally published in The Aquarian Teacher Yoga Manual

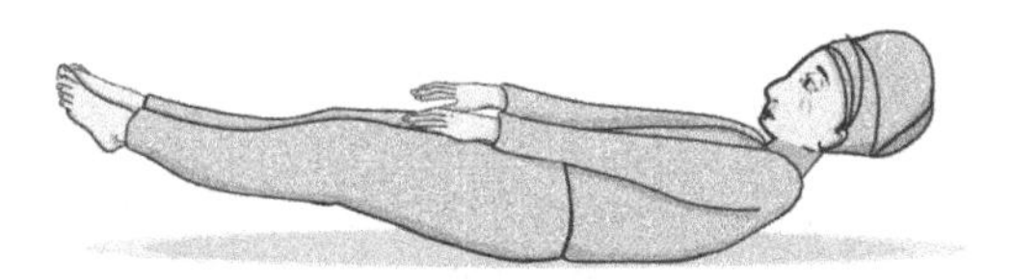

1) Stretch Pose. Lie on the back. Bend the knees and bring the legs towards the chest. Apply a strong Root Lock, engage the Navel Point and the sacrum, pressing the lower back against the ground. Inhale. Exhale and simultaneously stretch your legs straight so that the feet are 6 inches (15 cm) off the ground while you tuck the chin into the chest with Neck Lock, lengthening the neck. Look at the toes. Arms reach towards the feet, either alongside the body with palms facing the thighs or hands over the thighs, palms facing down. Continue for **1-3 minutes** with Breath of Fire.

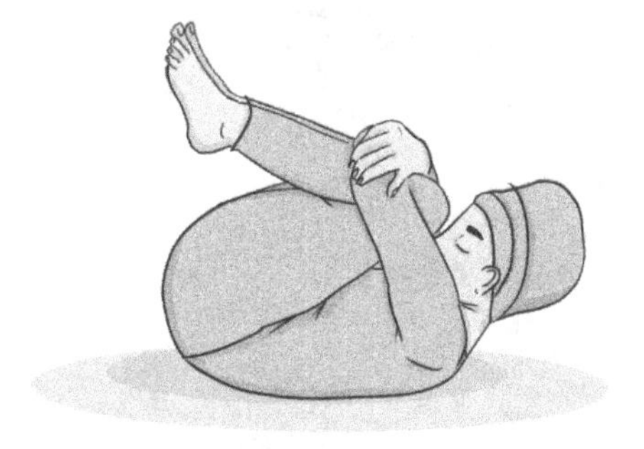

2) Nose to Knees. Lie on the back. Pull the knees into the chest, wrap the arms around the front of the legs just below the knees. Tuck the chin into the chest with the nose between the knees. Continue for **1-3 minutes** with Breath of Fire.

3) Ego Eradicator. Sit in Easy Pose with a straight spine and a light Neck Lock. Roll the shoulders down and open the shoulder blades wide. Raise the arms up and straight to 60 degrees. Curl the fingers onto the mounds at the base of the fingers, and stretch the palms wide, pulling knuckles back. Stretch the thumbs away from the fingers and point them straight up. With eyes closed, focus on the Third Eye Point, while concentrating above the head. Continue for **1-3 minutes** with Breath of Fire. TO END: Inhale, suspend the breath, touch the thumb tips together over the head. Open fingers wide. Exhale and apply Root Lock. Inhale, exhale, and slowly lower the arms. Relax.

4) Life Nerve Stretch. Sit with a straight spine and light Neck Lock. Sit tall on the sit bones, with the legs stretched wide apart, pelvis tilted slightly forward and thighs rolled inward. Inhale and stretch the arms straight up. Exhale, stretch down and over the left leg, grasping the toes. Elongate the spine as you stretch down from the hip joint. Do not let the spine collapse. Heart leads and head follows. Inhale, come up to center with the arms over head; then exhale and stretch down and over the right leg, grasping the toes. Continue alternating sides for **1-3 minutes**. Breathe powerfully.

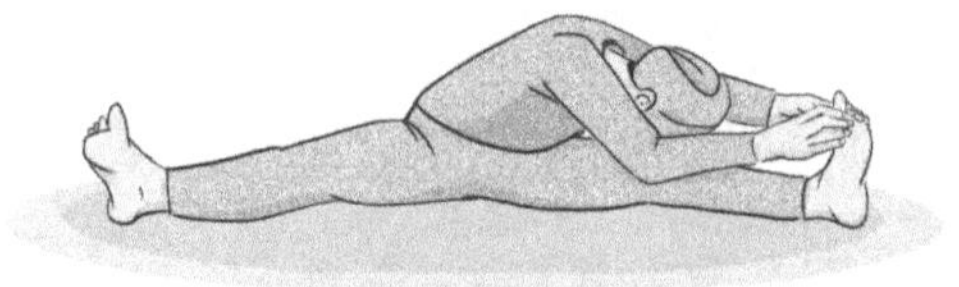

5) Life Nerve Stretch Forward Bend. Remain seated with the legs stretched wide apart. Grasp the toes of both feet, inhale elongate the spine, exhale stretch down, bringing the chest to the ground. Heart leads and the head follows. Inhale, come up to the center. Hands hold the toes throughout the movement. Continue for **1-3 minutes**. Breathe powerfully.

6) Spinal Flex (Camel Ride). Sit in Easy Pose with a straight spine and a light Neck Lock. Grasp the shins or ankles with the hands. Tilt the pelvis forward on the inhale, and backward on the exhale. Only the pelvis and lower spine move. The rib cage, shoulders and head are still and remain over the hips. The motion is fluid and continuous. Continue for **1-3 minutes**. Breathe powerfully.

7) Spinal Flex in Rock Pose. Sit on the heels in Rock Pose with a straight spine and a light Neck Lock. Place the hands flat on the thighs. Flex the spine forward and lift the chest on the inhale; flex the spine backward on the exhale. The movement is at the level of the solar plexus. The rib cage, shoulders and head are still and remain over the hips. Hands stay fixed on the thighs. Focus at the Third Eye Point. Continue for **1-3 minutes**.

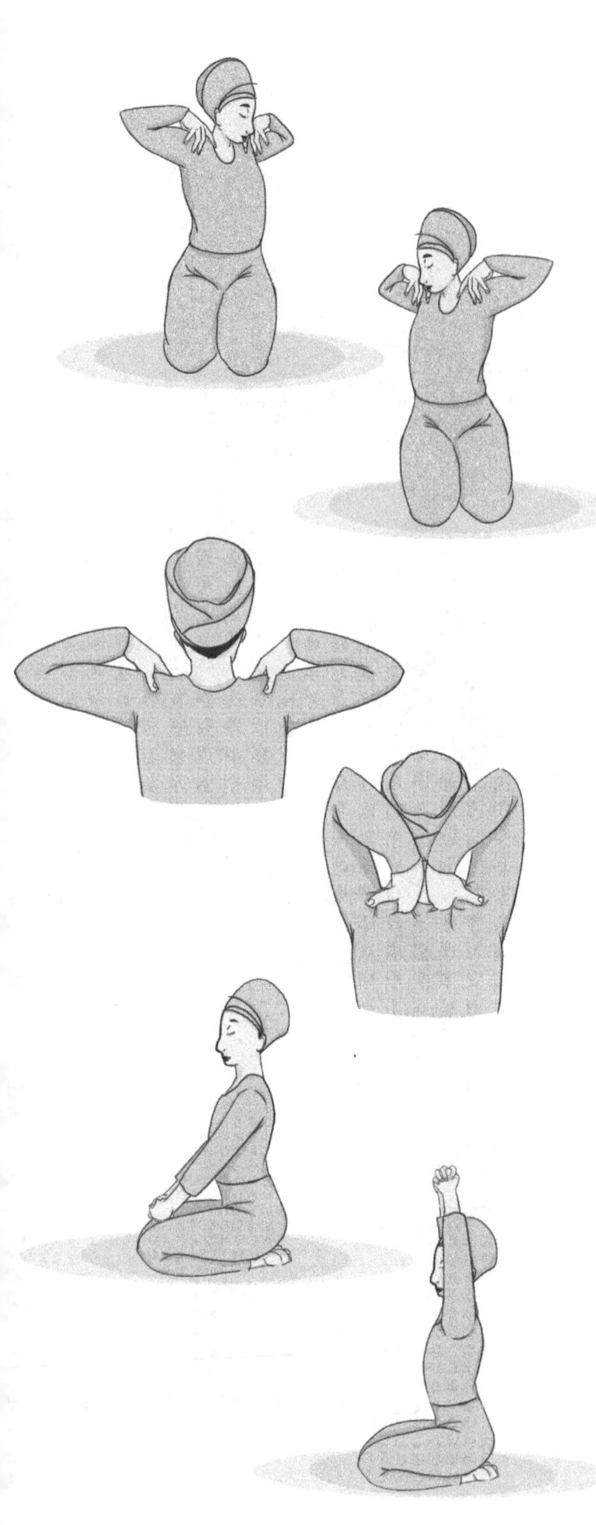

8) Spinal Twist in Rock Pose. Remain in Rock Pose with a straight spine and a light Neck Lock. Grasp the shoulders with the fingers in front, thumbs in back. Twist to the left on the inhale and twist to the right on the exhale. Keep the upper arms parallel to the ground, elbows pulled back to open the chest. Initiate the movement from the Navel Point, not the arms. Allow the head to move with the spine. Continue for **1-3 minutes**.

9) Elbows Raise. Remain in Rock Pose, grasp the shoulders as in the previous exercise. Raise the elbows up so that the wrists touch behind the neck on the inhale; lower the elbows to the starting position on the exhale. Continue for **1-3 minutes**. Breathe powerfully.

10) Arm Pumps. Remain in Rock Pose with a straight spine and a light Neck Lock. Interlock the fingers in Venus Lock. Stretch the arms straight up above the head on the inhale, and forcefully lower the arms just above the lap on the exhale. Keep the arms straight, elbows slightly locked. Continue for **1-3 minutes**. Move and breathe powerfully.

11) Alternate Shoulder Shrugs. Sit in Easy Pose with a straight spine and a light Neck Lock. Place the hands on the knees. Raise the left shoulder up as you lower the right shoulder on the inhale, and raise the right shoulder up as you lower the left shoulder on the exhale. Continue moving one shoulder up as the other comes down for **1 minute**. Then reverse the breath, raise the right shoulder up, left shoulder down on the inhale and raise the left shoulder up, right shoulder down on the exhale. Continue for **1 minute**. Breathe powerfully.

12) Shoulder Shrugs. Remain in Easy Pose with a straight spine and a light Neck Lock. Rest the hands on the knees. Raise both shoulders up towards the ears on the inhale, drop the shoulders down on the exhale. Continue for **1 minute**. Move and breathe powerfully.

13) Neck Turns. Remain in Easy Pose with a straight spine and a light Neck Lock. Place the hands on the knees. Turn the head to the left on the inhale, and to the right on the exhale. Continue for **1 minute**. Then reverse the breath, turn to the right on the inhale and left on the exhale. Continue for **1 minute**. TO END: Inhale at the center, focus at the Third Eye Point, and slowly exhale.

14) Frog Pose. Squat on the toes, with the knees wide and spine straight. Heels touch and are off the ground. Fingertips are on the ground between the legs and close to the body. The face is forward. Lift the hips and straighten the legs up on the inhale, keeping the fingertips on the ground. Squat down to the starting position on the exhale. Engage the Navel Point and use the fingertips on the ground for support. Keep the heels slightly off the ground throughout the exercise, and the knees always remain outside the arms. Continue this cycle **54 times**. Move rapidly and breathe powerfully.

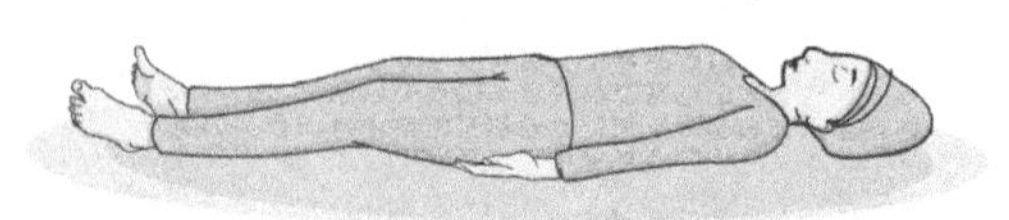

15) Relaxation. Deeply relax in Corpse Pose for **3-11 minutes**.

16) Laya Yoga Meditation Kriya. Sit in Easy Pose with a straight spine and a light Neck Lock. Place the hands on the knees in Gyan Mudra (thumb and index finger together.) Chant the mantra **EK ONG KAAR(UH) SAT NAAM(UH) SIREE WHAA(UH) HAY GUROO**. On "Ek" pull the Navel Point in lightly, and hold. Lift the diaphragm up firmly as you chant each line of the mantra. The "uh" sound is not a word; it is created as the diaphragm powerfully moves up. Relax the Navel Point and abdomen on "Hay Guroo". With the breath, visualize the sound or energy spiraling up from the base of the spine out the top of the head spinning in 3 ½ spins. (The spin is counterclockwise as though you are looking down at a clock on the ground.) Continue for **11-31 minutes**.

Breath In, Breath Out

Keep Up With Your Journey

LET YOUR INTUITION HAVE MORE SAY

Do you rely on your intuition? Humans have an innate system that computes the signals from the environment and returns information to us to help us understand any situation and make the best decisions. The information comes in many forms, and sometimes it's just a feeling, a vision or something subtle that is easy to dismiss without hard evidence. This is one reason why most people don't trust intuition or even think it's real, and it's certainly not part of most school curriculums.

But we yogis understand our connection to the universe and learn to trust our bodies, which is why it makes sense to develop intuition so we can always rely on ourselves. With your intuition intact, you cannot be manipulated. Kundalini Yoga associates human intuition with the pituitary gland, and this set activates the pituitary gland so it can serve you in any situation with the clarity to see both danger and solutions with no one else to tell you what is right or wrong.

KRIYA PITUITARY GLAND SERIES

Originally published in The Aquarian Teacher Yoga Manual

1) Lunge Stretch. Bend the right knee with the right foot on the ground. Extend the left leg straight back with the top of the foot flat on the ground. Place the hands on the ground for balance. Arch the head back and breathe slowly and deeply for **1 minute**. Continue for **2 more minutes** with Breath of Fire.

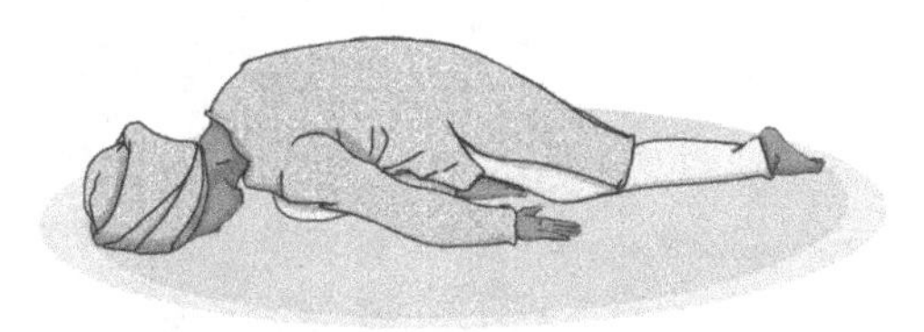

2) Lunge Stretch Rest. From position 1, bend the right knee with the lower leg resting on the ground. Bend forward from the hips bringing the torso over the thigh and the forehead (Third Eye Point) to the ground. The left leg remains extended straight back. The arms rest by the sides, palms facing up. Breath slowly and deeply for **3 minutes**.

3) Repeat exercises 1 and 2 with the opposite legs.

4) Forward Bend. Stand with the feet hip width apart. Inhale and elongate the spine, stretching the arms up. Exhale, bend forward from the hips, lengthening the torso, and touch the fingertips or the palms on the ground. Let the head, neck and arms relax. Continue with Long Deep Breathing for **3 minutes**.

5) Standing Ego Eradicator. Stand up and raise the arms up to a 30-degree angle.

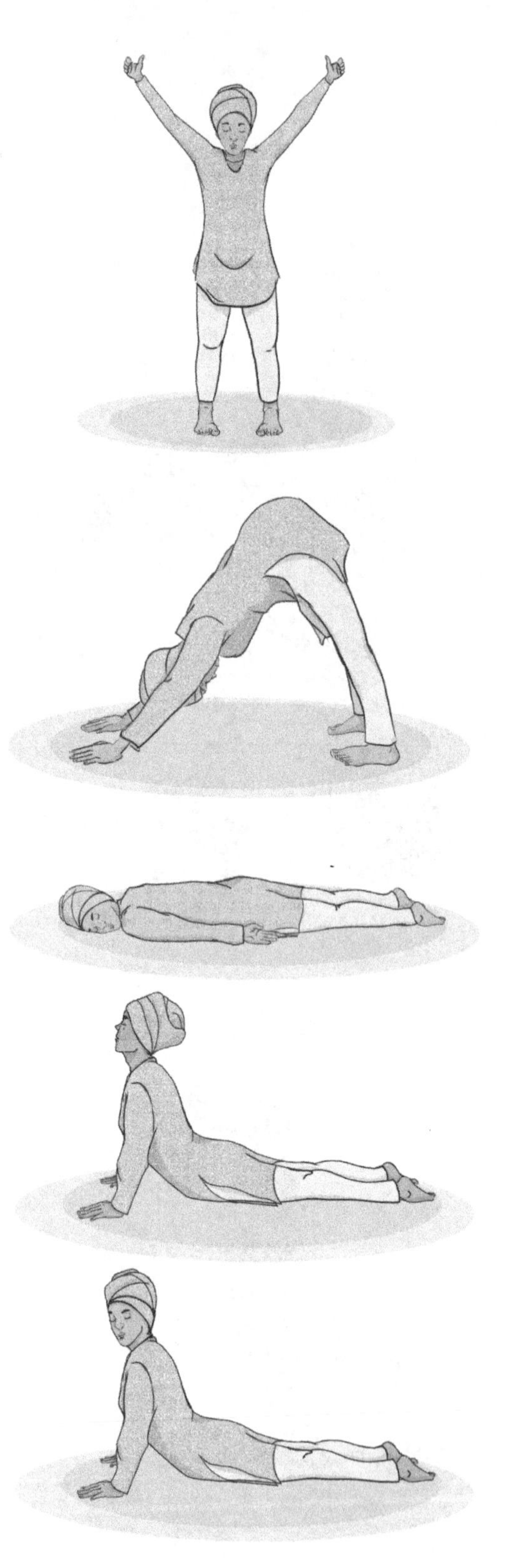

Curl the fingertips onto the mounds at the base of the fingers, pull the knuckles back, stretching the hands wide. The thumbs point up. Keep the elbows straight. Continue breathing long and deep for **3 minutes**.

6) Triangle Pose. Come onto hands and knees, with hands directly underneath the shoulders and knees directly underneath the hip joints. Lift the pelvis up by straightening the arms and legs, forming an upside down "V". Actively reach the shoulder blades down the back, and maintain a long neck by applying Neck Lock. Distribute the weight evenly between the hands and feet. Continue for **3 minutes**.

7) Cobra Pose with Variations. a) Lie on the stomach with the head to one side and arms at the sides, palms facing up. Remain resting on the stomach for **1 minute**.
b) Place the hands on the ground under the shoulders, and push up into Cobra Pose by elongating the spine, lifting the Heart Center, and dropping the shoulders away from the ears. Shoulder blades reach down and wide. Elbows are stretched but not locked. Continue for **1 minute** with Long Deep Breathing. **c)** Remain in Cobra Pose, turn the head from side to side, inhaling to the left, exhaling to the right. Continue for **2 minutes**.
TO END: Inhale, exhale, and apply Root Lock. Repeat **2 more times**.

8) Rock Pose Variation. Sit on the heels with the knees spread wide apart.

The heels are under the sit bones with the toes reaching straight back. Inhale as you rise up on the knees, stretching the arms up and out like a flower opening to the sun. Exhale sitting back on your heels and bending forward from the hip joint bringing the forehead (Third Eye Point) to the ground. The palms are flat on the ground in front of the knees. Continue the movement for **3 minutes**. *When coming up, keep a straight spine and avoid leaning back.*

9) Yoga Mudra. Sit in Rock Pose on the heels with knees together. Elongate the spine and bend forward from the hips bringing the torso over the thighs and the forehead (Third Eye Point) to touch the ground. Interlace the fingers at the base of the spine, palms facing up, and lift the arms up as far as possible. Draw the shoulders away from the ears and squeeze the shoulder blades together. The elbows are straight. Remain in this position for **3 minutes** with Long Deep Breathing.

RISE BEYOND THE GRAVITY OF SURVIVAL, SEX, AND POWER

It's fair to say that most of what is in the news these days has to do with money, sex, and power. These are also among the primary concerns of the first three chakras, those from the navel down that make up the lower triangle. They process issues in our lives related to survival and belonging; sexuality and creativity; personal power and projection.

Imbalances in the lower triangle can affect your life negatively, just as negative events in your life related to the lower triangle can make you unbalanced. From this perspective, it's easy to see how sexual violence can debase a person. Sat Kriya brings balance back into the lower triangle. It sorts out the physical and spiritual energy from the navel down, which translates into a healthier relationship with all related life issues and an accelerated personal evolution beyond your most basic concerns.

SAT KRIYA

Originally published in The Aquarian Teacher Yoga Manual

Sit on the heels in Rock Pose with a straight spine and a strong Neck Lock.

Mudra: Interlace the fingers with only the Jupiter (index) fingers pointing up and the thumbs crossed. For working with masculine, projective energy, place the right thumb over the left. For working feminine, reflective energy, place the left thumb over the right. Engage the Navel Point and root down from the navel into the earth. Let the rib cage rise while allowing the shoulders and shoulder blades to draw down and wide as you stretch the arms straight up overhead. Keep the elbows straight and the hands and arms continue stretching upwards for the duration of the exercise.

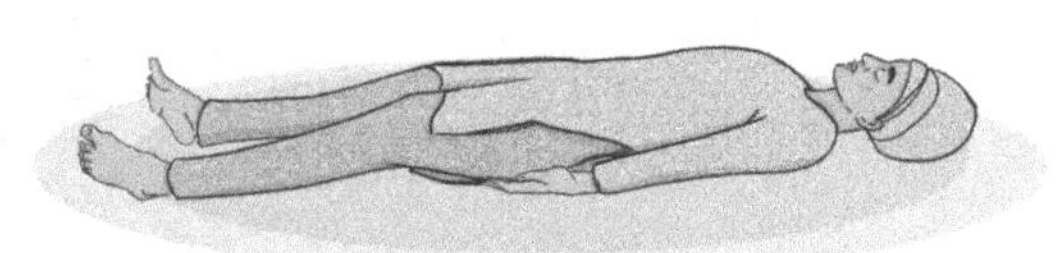

Mantra: Chant **SAT** and pull the Navel Point in and up. Chant **NAAM** as you release it.

Time: Continue rhythmically for **3-31 minutes**.

To End: Inhale, apply Root Lock and squeeze the muscles tightly from the buttocks all the way up the spine. Suspend the breath briefly as you concentrate on the area just above the top of the head. Mentally allow the energy to flow through the top of the skull. Exhale completely.

Inhale, exhale, suspend the breath for **5-20 seconds** and apply all three locks, the Great Lock (Root Lock, Diaphragm Lock and Neck Lock). Inhale and completely relax. Ideally the relaxation is twice the length of time that you practiced Sat Kriya.

Comments: Sat Kriya is an essential practice of Kundalini Yoga. It is one of the few exercises that is a kriya, a complete action in itself. Start with a daily 3 minutes practice. Over time, increase to **31 minutes**. Remember it is important to have a deep relaxation after this kriya. A good way to build the time up is to practice for **3 minutes**, then rest **2 minutes**. Repeat this cycle until you have completed **15 minutes** of Sat Kriya and **10 minutes** of rest. Finish the required relaxation by resting an additional **15-20 minutes**. Let the kriya prepare your body properly to plant the seed of higher experience. Prepare yourself with constancy, patience and moderation. The end result is assured.

• If you have not taken drugs or have cleared your system of all their effects, you may choose to practice this kriya with the palms open, pressing flat against each other. This releases more energy than the other method. It is generally not taught this way in a public class because someone in the class may have weak nerves from drug use.

• Emphasize pulling the Navel Point in and up. You don't need to try to apply Root Lock. Root Lock happens automatically when the Navel Point is pulled. Consequently, the hips and lumbar spine do not rotate or flex. Your spine stays straight and the only motion your arms make is a slight up-and-down stretch as your chest lifts.

• General physical health is improved since all the internal organs receive a gentle rhythmic massage from this exercise.

• If you have time for nothing else, make this kriya part of your daily promise to yourself to keep the body a clean and vital temple of God.

ANGER DOESN'T LIVE HERE ANYMORE

Anger lives in the space of sexual violence. Sometimes it stands right outside your door, sometimes it moves into the attic, hidden and quiet, yet permanent. It can be anger at the perpetrator, other people, or at yourself.

Either way, anger wears you down and invites disease. This kriya treats anger like the unwanted entity that it is and casts it out. Think of it as spiritual house cleaning. The kriya is not concerned with the story of how the anger got there, which makes it a universal kriya for all types of anger. For faster elimination of anger, add more green foods into your diet, as they cool the system, and try some of the cooling pranayama in Kundalini Yoga, such as left-nostril breathing.

KRIYA FOR RELIEVING INNER ANGER

September 21, 1988

1) Corpse Pose Snoring. Lie on the back in a relaxed posture with arms at the sides, palms up and legs slightly apart. Pretend to snore for **1 ½ minutes.** *Snoring relaxes the body.*

2) Anger Balance. Remain on the back. Engage the Navel Point, apply a light a Root Lock, and raise both legs 6 inches (15 cm) off the ground. Keep the legs together and straight. Hold for **2 minutes.** *This exercise pressurizes the Navel Point, brings anger to the surface and uses it to balance the whole body.*

3) Leg Raise with Lion's Breath. Remain in the posture, stretch out the tongue and do Breath of Fire from the throat. Continue for **1 ½ minutes.**

4) Beat the Ground. Remain on the back and raise the legs up to 90 degrees. The arms are on the ground by your sides, palms down. Keeping the arms stiff and straight, move from the shoulders and beat the ground with all the anger you can achieve. Beat hard and fast. Continue for **2 ½ minutes.**

5) Knees to Chest. Remain on the back, bring the knees into the chest and wrap your arms around them. Stretch the tongue out. Inhale through the mouth and exhale through the nose. Continue for **2 minutes**.

6) Bowing in Celibate Pose. Sit in Celibate Pose (sit on the heels, open the knees placing the feet at the sides of the hips and sit with buttocks on the ground between the legs). Hold opposite elbows, press the arms firmly against the rib cage. Bend forward from the hips and touch your forehead to the ground and then come back up. Continue for **2 ½ minutes**, moving at a pace of approximately 30 bows per minute. Then for another **30 seconds** speed up and move as fast as you can.

7) Self-Massage. Sit with your legs straight out in front of you. Begin to hit every part of your body with open palms. Move quickly for **2 minutes**.

8) Standing U. Standing, bend forward, keep the back straight and parallel to the ground, and let the arms and hands hang loose. Remain in this posture and sing. Continue for **3 minutes**. (A recording of **GUROO GUROO WHAA-HAY GUROO GUROO RAM DAS GUROO** was played in the original class.)

9) Cobra Variations with Singing. Place the hands on the ground under the shoulders, and come into Cobra Pose and continue singing for **1 minute**. Still in Cobra and singing, circle the head for **30 seconds.** Still in Cobra, moving from the knees, kick the ground with alternate feet for **30 seconds.**

10) Sat Kriya in Easy Pose. Sit in Easy Pose with a straight spine and a light Neck Lock and close your eyes. Interlace the fingers with only the Jupiter (index) fingers pointing up and the thumbs crossed. Stretch the arms straight up overhead. Keep the elbows straight. Chant **SAT** and pull the Navel Point in and up. Chant **NAAM** as you release it. Continue for **1 ½ minutes.**

11) Corpse Pose. Relax on the back with arms by your sides and palms facing up, nap for at least **5 minutes.**

Comments: One effect of inner anger is the inability to have a relationship with oneself. Manipulation, lying, inferiority and superiority complexes are different manifestations of inner anger. On the other hand, it's important to note that the heat of the anger can be used either to transform your life or hold you back.

SET YOUR RECEIVER TO UNIVERSAL WISDOM

This kriya is also called "Earth to Heaven", and it's clear from the up-and-down movement of your fingertips that you are establishing a line of communication from your grounded physical self to your infinite higher self. That means you can receive wisdom from above and develop a clear knowing that is anchored in your true nature and gives you the self-autonomy to assess and excel in any situation.

You set the dial in just the right place by using our index fingers, which channel Jupiter energy, the source of the most graceful knowledge. You also remove static in your reception by clearing out even more anger, just like on day 4.

HAST KRIYA: EARTH TO HEAVEN

January 31, 1996

Sit in Easy Pose with a straight spine and a light Neck Lock.

Mudra: Make fists with both hands with the Jupiter (index) fingers extended and the other fingers held down with the thumbs. Synchronize the movements with the mantra. Touch the ground by the sides of the body on "Sat" and "Whaa-Hay". Keep the arms straight. Touch the tips of the finger above the head, forming an arc with the arms, on "Naam" and "Guroo". One complete cycle takes 6-7 seconds. Concentrate on the fingertips touching.

Eye Focus: Closed.

Breath: Not specified.

Mantra: SAT NAAM SAT NAAM, WHAA-HAY GUROO WHAA-HAY GUROO (In the original class, "Sat Nam Wahe Guru #2" by Jagjit Singh was played.)

Time: 22 minutes.

Comments: This kriya renews the nervous system and can help nerve pain and sciatica. If you do this kriya for 22 minutes a day, anger and obnoxiousness can be dissolved. Sat Naam Whaa-hay Guroo is a powerful Jupiter mantra. In

Vedic astrology, Jupiter is considered to be the second most powerful planet, known for compassion, generosity, tolerance, growth and expansion; and responsible for knowledge, dedication and wisdom. It influences spiritual growth by maintaining optimism.

Breath In, Breath Out
Keep Up With Your Journey

FIND THE CALM AT THE CENTER OF THE HURRICANE

We all share a physical world that is louder and busier than ever. That's stressful enough, but even more stressful is trying to control all these fast-moving parts. It's like flying a little plane through a giant storm with a thousand blinking lights all around you in the cockpit. It's an almost impossible feat, yet that's the strategy of most people, and that's why everyone is exhausted and so many crash.

The brilliance of yoga is that it recognizes the outside world as a reflection of your inner world and delivers technologies to control the inner world — the only factor you have complete control over. This kriya is an example of such a technology. It places you at the control center of your glandular system with a recipe for optimal body chemistry that makes you feel calm and centered, no matter what happens around you. Try it, then watch the universe adapt to your powerful inner peace and quiet your outer world accordingly.

KRIYA COMMANDING THE COMMAND CENTER OF THE GLANDULAR SYSTEM

May 19, 1993

PART ONE

Sit in Easy Pose with a straight spine and a light Neck Lock.

Mudra: Stretch the right arm straight forward at shoulder level, parallel to the ground, with the palm facing down. The left elbow is out to the side; place the fingertips of the left hand in a vertical line in the center of the forehead. The Mercury (little) finger is at the level of the eyebrows. The left fingers are curved so that the fingertips touch the forehead and the thumb is separated from the other fingers and pointing up like an antenna. Pump the navel as fast as you can. The whole body must shake with the power of the navel movement.

Eye Focus: Closed.

Breath: You may choose to do this with or without Breath of Fire.

Time: 3 minutes.

To End: Take three full, deep breaths. Inhale deeply, exhale, suspend the breath out for **10 seconds**, squeeze all the muscles, let the body shake, and inhale. Repeat this sequence **2 more times** and relax.

PART TWO

Remain in Easy Pose.

Mudra: Stretch the arms straight forward, bend the elbows slightly, and cup the hands with the palms facing up. Tilt the head back a little, with an "O" shaped mouth. Relax the lips, teeth, and tongue. Pump your navel vigorously.

Breath: Not specified.

Eye Focus: Not specified.

Time: 3 minutes.

To End: Inhale, suspend the breath for **20 seconds**, lock your back molars and tighten your jaw, exhale. Repeat the sequence **2 more times**. Relax.

PART THREE

Remain in Easy Pose.

Mudra: Stretch the arms straight forward, parallel to the ground, palms facing each other with the fingers together and the thumbs relaxed. Without bending the elbows, crisscross the arms rapidly in front of the chest on the suspended inhalation. Each arm alternately passes above and below the other.

Eye Focus: Not specified.

Breath: Inhale deeply, suspend the breath for **20 seconds** while you rapidly crisscross the arms, exhale.

Time: 3 minutes.

To End: Lie on the back in Corpse Pose and relax deeply. Relax every part of the body and let it recuperate.

Comments: In the Age of Aquarius, depression and stress may harm people who do not have the technical knowledge of the Self. Experience how quickly neurosis can leave you. This kriya cleans the subconscious mind through stimulating the pituitary gland, the master gland that is responsible for intuition and projection.

UNDERSTAND WHO YOU ARE

When someone asks you who you are, you'll probably mention some labels from a list you've compiled over time, like profession, education, age, background, and so on. Does the list include: "Spiritual being connected to the entire universe and co-creating reality?" It should, at the top of the list.

Kundalini Yoga, like other spiritual teachings, says that a spiritual being is exactly who you are, and that the main reason for all human pain in the world is that we have forgotten our true identity. Your own depression might very well be related to that kind of disempowered self-identity. This kriya wakes you up to who you really are and the power you possess. Expect to shake as if you are being electrocuted, and imagine being plugged into universal consciousness, your primary power source, so that your individual consciousness can light up and shine in the universe like the bright star that it is.

About the effects of this class, Yogi Bhajan said it helps you realize who you are. He went on to say, "Life starts from the day that you realize who you are. From that day onward, you want to build who you should be. When you have built to the extent that you are who you should be, from then onward, you have the right to overflow and share".

A VERY SUBTLE EXERCISE

Getting to the Root of Subconscious Depression

February 20, 1985

There is no break between exercises.

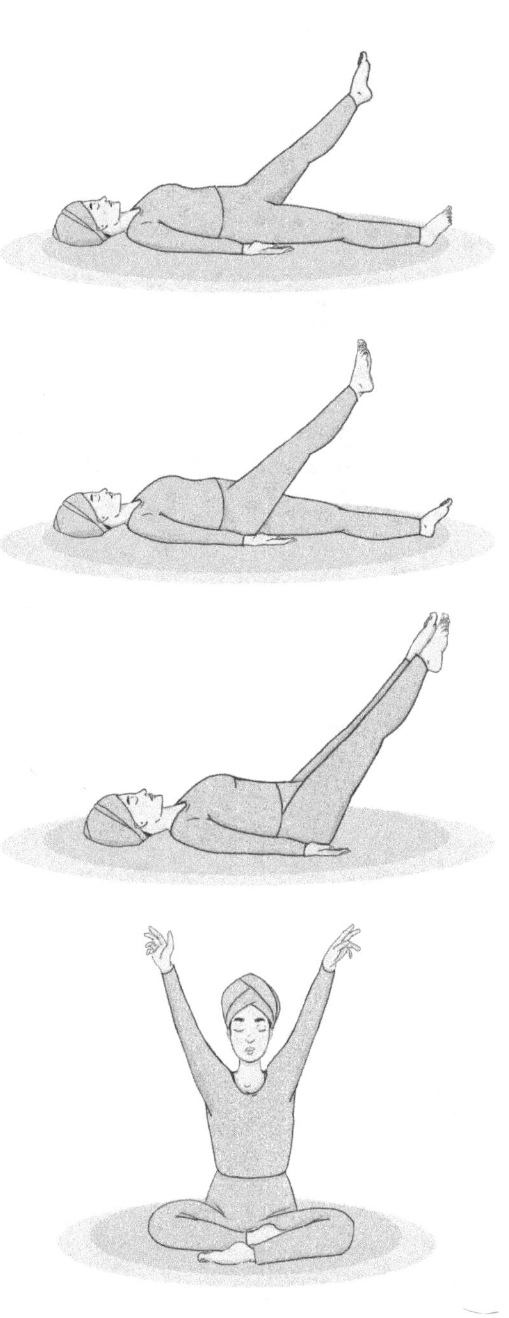

1) Shake Leg – Left. Lie on the back, with your arms by your sides. Raise the left leg up to 60 degrees and shake it vigorously while relaxing the rest of your body. Keep both legs straight. Continue for **3 minutes**.

2) Shake Leg – Right. Remain lying on your back. Switch legs and shake the right leg. Shake it harder than you shook the left leg, while relaxing the rest of your body. Continue for **3 minutes**.

3) Shake Legs – Both. Remain lying on your back. Raise both legs up to 60 degrees and vigorously shake them. Keep your knees straight. Continue for **3 minutes**.

4) Shake Hands — From Wrists. Sit in Easy Pose with a straight spine and a light Neck Lock. Raise both arms straight up and vigorously shake your hands moving from the wrists. Close your eyes and concentrate on the pineal gland by focusing your internal gaze at the top center of your head. Continue for **7 ½ minutes**. Meditate deeply, listening to

14 A RECORDING OF "YOU ARE MY LOVER, LORD" IS PART OF KRISHNA KAUR'S ALBUM ONE CREATOR AND IS AVAILABLE AT SPIRIT VOYAGE, GURBANI MEDIA CENTER, APPLE MUSIC AND SPOTIFY.

the song "You Are My Lover, Lord"[14] by Krishna Kaur, which was played in the original class.

5) Meditation. Remain in Easy Pose. Place your hands in your lap with eyes closed. Breathe slowly with long deep breaths. Continue to meditatively listen to the music "You are my Lover, Lord" for **9 minutes**. To End: Inhale, suspend the breath as long as you can and meditate for a maximum of **1 minute**. Hold without creating too much pressure. Cannon fire exhale, suspend the breath as long as you can (for a maximum of **30 seconds**) while you powerfully pull the navel inward. Inhale and relax.

Comments: These 5 exercises stimulate the whole glandular system. To experience long-term positive changes in your life, try practicing this kriya every morning for one week. At the end of the kriya, write down the time and how you feel, and later in the evening, write down the time and how the day went. After a week, assess how you have changed.

Breath In, Breath Out
Keep Up With Your Journey

A FAST WAY HOME

Just like on the previous day, the activation of your true identity is the goal today. This kriya quickly breaks through the crust that has formed around your true self by the ego. Think of the ego here as everything that locks your identity in physical forms like your body and possessions – including the thought-forms you carry, like your life story and the related opinions, beliefs, preferences and fears that you have developed, rather than an identity formed in spirit.

The experience of sexual violence especially can harden this crust into a thick shell that thoroughly hides your true formless spiritual identity and makes you forget how powerful you are. With energizing breath, arms positioned in a sign of victory as extensions of your heart, and eyes at your center of intuition, this kriya is a shortcut to your true self and a classic asana and warm-up in Kundalini Yoga. Try it for three minutes every day.

EGO ERADICATOR

Originally published in The Aquarian Teacher Yoga Manual

Sit in Easy Pose with a straight spine and a light Neck Lock.

Mudra: Roll the shoulders down and open the shoulder blades wide. Raise the arms up and straight to 60 degrees. Curl the fingers onto the mounds at the base of the fingers and pull the knuckles back, stretching the palms wide. Draw the thumbs away from the fingers and point them straight up. Keep the neck and shoulder muscles relaxed, and maintain straight arms and the 60 degree angle.

Eye Focus: Closed, focus on the Third Eye Point, while concentrating above the head.

Breath: Breath of Fire.

Time: 3 minutes (minimum).

To End: Inhale, suspend the breath, keep the arms straight; bring the tips of the thumbs together over the head. Uncurl the fingers and stretch them wide. Elongate the spine and focus above the head. Exhale and apply Root Lock. Inhale, exhale, release the Root Lock and slowly lower the arms. Relax.

Comments: Breath of Fire cleanses the lungs and the respiratory system, while the posture stretches the Lung Meridian[15], and brings the hemispheres of the brain to a state of alertness.

15 IN CHINESE MEDICINE, THE LUNG MERIDIAN DEFENDS THE EXTERIOR SURFACE OF THE BODY, PROTECTING IT AGAINST OUTSIDE PATHOGENS, INCLUDING EXCESS WIND, HEAT OR DAMPNESS.

LEARN TO SMILE LIKE BUDDHA

If you believe that everything you want – including your healing and well-being – can only come from hard work, think again. There is tremendous power in taking a simple path, so please take a break today from long kriyas with vigorous movements and practice the Smiling Buddha Kriya instead.

Everything about this meditation is soft and easy, like floating down a river on a warm summer day. But don't underestimate its power. It is said that Buddha and Christ practiced this meditation, and you might recognize the mudra from paintings and statues of both of them.

SMILING BUDDHA KRIYA

October 7, 1972

Sit in Easy Pose with a straight spine and a light Neck Lock.

Mudra: Make fists with the Jupiter (index) and Saturn (middle) fingers extended, and the other fingers held down with the thumbs. The elbows are at the sides of the body and pressed back by drawing the shoulder blades towards each other. The forearms are up and parallel to each other, 30 degrees in front of the shoulders. The palms face forward. Mentally chant the mantra at the Third Eye Point.

Breath: Not specified.

Eye Focus: Third Eye Point.

Mantra: Mentally chant the Panj Shabad, **SAA TAA NAA MAA,** at the Third Eye Point.

Time: 11 minutes.

To End: Inhale deeply, exhale, open and close the fists several times. Relax.

Comments: Panj Shabad: Saa (Infinite), Taa (Life, existence), Naa (Death), Maa (Regeneration, light). These are the bij (seed) sounds of Sat Naam, which means, "I am Truth." You have probably seen images, statues or paintings of Christ and Buddha with this same hand mudra or gesture. It is a gesture and exercise of happiness and it opens the flow of the Heart Center. Master the technique and experience the state of higher consciousness that it brings. Then share it by creating beauty and peace.

Breath In, Breath Out
Keep Up With Your Journey

DROP THE HEAVY CARGO OF FEAR

For those days when fear takes over you and you can't find a way out, keep this kriya handy. It's a longer kriya and quite a workout, but it's one of the best investments you can make in your emotional well-being, because its effects can be immediate. On a physical level, this set massages the liver and kidneys, the storehouses of fear and related negative psychological states.

The brilliant combination of dance-like movements, cleansing pranayama and hypnotic meditations takes you on a journey through peaks and valleys and leaves your fears behind so you can arrive at an experience of your life that is sunny, secure, and under your control.

KRIYA TO RELAX AND RELEASE FEAR

Originally taught in the summer of 1983

1) Standing Cat-Cow. Stand up and bend forward from the hips, keeping the back parallel to the ground. Reach behind your legs and hold on to your calves or whatever you can reach to maintain your balance. Begin to flex the spine as in Cat-Cow posture. Inhale and arch your back downward, lowering the belly, lifting the sternum and chin and broadening the collarbones. Keep the back of the neck long. Exhale and round your spine upward, bringing the chin to the chest. Use the hands and feet as a firm base of support for the spine. Keep the arms and legs straight. Maintain a steady rhythm for **7 minutes**. *This exercise works on the kidneys and liver.*

2) Standing Torso Circles. Remain standing with a straight spine and a light Neck Lock. Place the hands on the hips. Rapidly rotate the torso in large circles from the hips. Continue for **9 minutes**. *This exercise rejuvenates the spleen and releases toxins from the liver.*

3) Spinal Twist Variation. Sit in Easy Pose with a straight spine and a light Neck Lock. Make fists and place them in front of you with the hands about 6 inches apart (15 cm), the forearms parallel to the ground, and elbows out to the sides. Twist to the left on the inhale and twist to the right on the exhale. Keep the elbows up and let the neck move. Twist the body for **4 minutes** with powerful breathing.

This exercise works on the kidneys. The neck movement releases the blood supply to the brain.

4) One Hand Clapping. Remain in Easy Pose. Stretch the arms up at a 60-degree angle, palms facing up, fingers straight pointing to the sides and thumbs extended out. Begin to open and close the hands rapidly, bringing the tips of the fingers to the base of the palms. Continue for **7 minutes**.
This exercise breaks up deposits in the fingers and prevents arthritis. If you already have arthritis, it may work on improving it.

5) Fists to Shoulders. Remain in Easy Pose. Touch the thumbs to the fleshy mound at the base of the Mercury (little) fingers and make fists, folding the fingers over the thumbs. Stretch the arms out to the sides, parallel to the ground. Bend the elbows, bringing the fists to the shoulders on the inhale and straighten the arms out to the sides on the exhale. Move rapidly and breathe powerfully through an "O" mouth. Continue for **6 minutes**.
This exercise removes tension from the neck and purifies the blood. In this exercise your fears will leave you when you powerfully project out on the exhale.

6) Fist Circles. Remain in Easy Pose with the hands in fists. Extend the arms straight forward and parallel to the ground at the level of the Heart Center, palms facing down. Rotate the fists in small outward circles. Keep the elbows straight, fists tight, and move from the wrists. Move the shoulder blades and the muscles underneath the shoulder area. Continue powerfully for **2 minutes**. *This exercise adjusts the muscles under the breasts. If this area is tight, it makes you very uptight.*

7) Crow Pose. Stand with the feet hip width apart. Apply Root Lock and Neck Lock to keep the spine elongated. Squat down, keeping the spine as perpendicular to the ground as possible. Make fists of the hands, bend the elbows, and place the fists near the sides of the neck, just above the shoulders. Inhale as you stand up and exhale as you squat down into a Crow Pose; fists stay in place throughout the movement. Continue for **3 minutes**.

8) Sitali Pranayam. Sit in Easy Pose with a straight spine and a light Neck Lock. Curl the tongue into a "U" shape and extend it slightly past the lips. Inhale deeply through the curled tongue, exhale through the nose. Breathe long and deeply for **4-5 minutes**. Then continue this breath in rhythm with healing music for **2 minutes**. (In the original class, a recording of "Dukh Bhanjan" was played[16].)

16 THE SHABAD "DUKH BHAJAN" IS A SACRED SIKH SONG IN PRAISE OF THE HEALING WATER THAT SURROUNDS THE GOLDEN TEMPLE IN AMRITSAR, INDIA. THE GOLDEN TEMPLE IS A BEAUTIFUL TEMPLE IN AMRITSAR, INDIA, THAT IS THE MOST SACRED SHRINE OF THE SIKHS. IT IS AN OPEN HOUSE OF WORSHIP FOR ALL PEOPLE, AND IS SURROUNDED ON ALL SIDES BY A TANK OF WATER. THE GOLDEN TEMPLE REPRESENTS A PLACE OF PRAYER AND HEALING FOR MANY.

Sitali Pranayam is effective against anger, bad moods and temperament. If your mouth becomes bitter, it means you are releasing toxins.

9) Sitting Dance. Remain in Easy Pose and raise the arms in a relaxed way above the head. Close the eyes and rhythmically move your arms and body to the music, without thinking. Keep the arms above the shoulder level and dance with the upper body for **10 minutes**. (In the original class, "Dukh Bhanjan" was played.) *If you can bring your body into exact rhythm with the music, you can go into a state of ecstasy.*

10) Bowing Jaap Sahib. Sit on the heels in Rock Pose, with hands on thighs. Listen to a musical recording of Jaap Sahib, sit meditatively for the first stanza and bring the forehead to the ground every time you hear "Namastang" or "Namo". Without the recording, the movement is done to 10 beats as follows: Bow down and come up in 2 counts for 4 cycles, and rest in the starting position, on counts 9 and 10. Continue for **8 minutes**. ("Jaap Sahib", by Ragi Sat Nam Singh was originally played in class).

11) Venus Lock Meditation. Sit in Easy Pose with a straight spine and a light Neck Lock. Interlace the fingers in Venus Lock, place them on the back of the head, with the elbows out to the sides. Apply pressure with the hands, keeping the spine straight. Close your eyes and chant out loud with the musical "Jaap Sahib" recording, copy the very essence of it and feel the vibrations going through your hands to the back of the head. If the recording is not available, breathe long and gently in this position. Continue for **8 minutes**. *Relax. Become calm. Feel that you are going to achieve God's Light in you. Totally remove any difference between yourself and God.*

MANAGE YOUR INNER AND OUTER FLOW

The essence of yoga – a conscious life in union with everything – is in almost every detail of the practice. For example, when we say as we did earlier that the outer world reflects the inner world, it's just another way of saying that everything is one. The same applies when we talk about the parallels between spiritual and physical processes, like the relationship between chakras and organs. They, too, are part of a larger system, and only our interpretation separates them into two.

This kriya is another opportunity to bring seemingly separate pieces together, the lymphatic system and a sense of flow in your whole life. The set supports the movement of cleansing fluids inside your body, and as things flow gently and freely inside of you, other pieces of your life can too.

KRIYA FOR THE LYMPHATIC SYSTEM

Originally published in Youth & Joy

1) Spinal Twist Variation. Sit in Easy Pose with a straight spine and a light Neck Lock. Interlace the fingers in Venus Lock and place them underneath the hairline. Stretch the elbows out to the sides, parallel to the ground, with the forearms parallel to the ground. Twist from side to side in a 4 count motion — left, center, right, center. Keep the elbows open and up. Inhale to each side and exhale to the center (2 seconds per cycle). Continue for **9 minutes.**
This helps remove tension from the shoulders and relaxes the muscles of the breasts.

2) Knee Raises. Remain in Easy Pose, grasp the outside of the knees. With the power of the hands pull the knees up towards each other on the inhale and let them drop down on the exhale (1 cycle takes less than 1 second). Continue for **6 minutes.**
This exercise applies tremendous pressure to the breast and stomach area. It also works on breaking down the fat around the abdomen and adjusts the ankles and knees.

3) Legs Kicks. Sit with a straight spine and a Light Neck Lock. Stretch both legs straight forward. Place the hands on the ground behind the body with fingers pointing backwards. Keeping the arms straight, lean back with your weight on the arms. Bring the knees into the body and kick out alternate lower legs. Move rapidly and powerfully keeping the ankles and feet relaxed. Continue for **3 minutes.** *This works on the lower spine.*

4) Pulling Arms Inward. Sit in Easy Pose with a straight spine and a light Neck Lock. Extend the arms forward at a slight outward angle, parallel to the ground, with the palms facing up. Alternately, make fists of the hands and pull straight back on the exhale. Pull hard enough to make the body shake. Move rapidly for **1-2 minutes**. The breath becomes like a Breath of Fire. *This works on opening up the arteries.*

5) Body Drop Variation. Remain in Easy Pose. Make fists and place the flat part of the fists on the ground next to the hips. Keeping the back straight, feet on the ground, lift the body up and then drop it down (1-2 times per second). Continue for **4 minutes**. *This builds up the shoulder muscles so that the lower torso is able to relax.*

6) Seated Side Bends. Remain in Easy Pose. Hold onto the knees and bend side to side from the waist. Bend completely, stretching a little further with each bend (2-3 seconds per cycle). Continue for **5-6 minutes**. *This aids in digestion.*

7) Head Bends. Remain in Easy Pose with the hands on the knees. Bend your head and mentally chant in this sequence: forward on **SAA**, back on **TAA**, to the left **NAA** and to the right **MAA**, returning to the center after each bend. Continue rhythmically, coordinating the movement with the mantra for **2-3 minutes**. *This strengthens the neck.*

8) Spinal Flex with Lion Lick. Remain in Easy Pose with the hands on the knees. Begin flexing your upper or thoracic spine forwards and backwards. Inhale through the nose as you flex forward, mouth closed. Exhale, draw the chin to the chest, stick the tongue out and make the sound "Hunh" as you flex backward. (1 second per cycle approximately.) Continue rhythmically for **3 minutes**. *This works on opening up the lungs.*

9) Half Stands. Squat in Crow Pose with the feet shoulder width apart and the toes facing slightly out. Place the hands on the knees, and come halfway up keeping the feet flat on the ground. (1 second per cycle approximately.) Continue rhythmically for a maximum of **8 minutes**, resting when needed. *This works directly on the knees. If the knees lose their elasticity, it can affect the alignment of the whole body.*

10) Feet Flexes. Sit with a straight spine and a light Neck Lock. Stretch both legs straight out in front with hands on the thighs. Alternately point both feet forward and flex both feet backward. (1-2 seconds.) Continue for **1 minute**. *This strengthens the muscles of the lower legs.*

11) Sufi Grinds. Sit in Easy Pose with a straight spine and a light Neck Lock. Place the hands on the knees. Lift the rib cage to open the space between the rib cage and the pelvis. Rotate the pelvis, inhaling as the pelvis circles forward and exhaling as the pelvis circles backwards. Only the pelvis, lower spine and abdomen move; the rib cage, shoulders, neck and head stay stable. Roll only to the right. (1-2 seconds per rotation.) Continue for **3-4 minutes**. *This works on digestion.*

12) Head Shakes. Remain sitting in Easy Pose with the hands on the knees. Rapidly begin shaking the head from left to right in short, sharp movements. Allow all the muscles of the mouth and face to relax. Continue for **3 minutes**. *As you loosen up and shake, the entire head area will move. It brings the blood to the capillaries and strengthens the cheek and jaw muscles.*

13) Hands Shake. Remain in Easy Pose with a straight spine. Extend the arms forward at chest level with a little bend in the elbows. The arms, hands and fingers are relaxed. Rapidly shake the hands in and out, keeping the wrists loose. Shake so fast that the fingers cut through the air and the hands feel separate from the body. Continue for **2-3 minutes**. *This is excellent for the sciatic nerve. It stimulates circulation and removes toxins.*

14) Meditation. Remain in Easy Pose with a straight spine. Place the hands in the lap. Chant with the tip of the tongue (2-3 seconds): **HAR, HAR, HAR, HAR, HAR, HAR, HAR, HARI.** Draw in the Navel Point each time the tip of the tongue touches the upper palate behind the front teeth. Continue chanting rhythmically for **3-4 minutes**. TO END: Stretch the arms over the head. Interlace the fingers of both hands with the palms facing up. Lean back and begin stretching from side to side like a cat. Continue for **1 minute**. *This is a meditation for endurance.*

16) Chant. Remain in Easy Pose with a straight spine. Chant the phrases in the following sequence:

"God and Me, Me and God, Are One". Continue for **3 minutes**.

"I Am Thee, Thou Is Me, Me Is Thou". Continue for **2-3 minutes**.

"All Things Come From God and All Things Go To God". Continue for **2 minutes**. *These 3 phrases are to be chanted in English, rather than translated in other languages.*

Breath In, Breath Out
Keep Up With Your Journey

REMOVE BODY BLOCKS

The title of the kriya is the motto of the day, and after we started the flow of fluids on the previous day, we get rid of bigger physical blockages inside our bodies today. Whether you know any specific ones inside of you or not, the following simple mental image will help: Picture a square, then picture the square being cut diagonally into two triangles from the top left corner to the bottom right. No longer a square but two triangles, the top triangle cannot stay where it is and slides right off the bottom triangle. Now think of this kriya cutting clunky energetic squares inside of you into ever smaller pieces that slide right out of your path, and the variety of positions and movement hits your blocks from many different angles. And as we remove blocks inside our body, we cut through all kinds of nonsense that collects when the natural flow of energy is blocked.

KRIYA FOR REMOVING BODY BLOCKS

March 19, 1986

There are no breaks between the exercises.

1) Arms Circles. Sit in Easy Pose with a straight spine and a light Neck Lock. Stretch the arms straight up, hands relaxed and facing forward. Move the arms above the head in large counterclockwise circles. Maintain the distance between the arms and move fast for **4 ½ minutes.** *This movement opens up your shoulders.*

2) Bowing with Straight Arms. Remain in Easy Pose with the arms stretched up and palms forward. Bend down touching the hands and forehead to the ground and rise back up. Move rapidly for **2 ½ minutes**.

3) Jumping on All Fours. Stand up, bend forward and place the hands on the ground. Jump up — both hands and both feet lift off the ground at the same time. Concentrate and use the strength of the navel to jump. Continue for **2 ½ minutes.**

4) Miracle Bend Variation. Stand up with the feet hip width apart and stretch the arms up straight, palms forward. Bend forward, touch the ground and look back through your legs. Rise up and bend backward. Continue this movement for **1 minute**.

5) Crisscross Jumps. Remain in a standing position and place the hands on the hips. Jump crisscrossing the legs, alternate which leg is in front. Move rapidly for **2 minutes**.

6) Crisscross Arms and Legs. Remain in a standing position and stretch the arms straight up. Jump crisscrossing the arms and the legs, alternating which arm and leg are in front. Balance and move rapidly for **2 minutes**.

7) Shoulder Rolls. Sit in Easy Pose with a straight spine and a light Neck Lock. Raise the elbows out to the side at shoulder level and bring the hands in front of the chest. The hands are curled, hanging relaxed from the wrists. Lift the shoulders up with tension while rolling alternate shoulders forward, letting the body twist naturally as the shoulders roll forward and back. Continue for **1 minute.**

8) Stretch Pose. Lie on the back. Bend the knees and bring the legs towards the chest. Apply a strong Root Lock, engage the Navel Point and the sacrum, pressing the lower back against the ground. Inhale. Exhale and simultaneously stretch your legs straight so that the feet are 6 inches (15 cm) off the ground while you tuck the chin into the chest with Neck Lock, lengthening the neck. Look at the toes. Arms reach towards the feet, either alongside the body with palms facing the thighs or hands over the thighs, palms facing down. Continue for **1 ½ minutes** with Breath of Fire.

9) Back Rolls. Remain on the back. Pull the knees into the chest, wrap the arms around the front of the legs just below the knees. Tuck the chin into the chest with the nose between the knees. Roll back and forth on your spine for **30 seconds**.

10) Back Rolls in Lotus Pose. Sit in Lotus Pose and hold onto the legs or feet. Roll back and forth on your spine for **1 ½ minutes.** (If you cannot come into Lotus Pose, come into Easy Pose.)

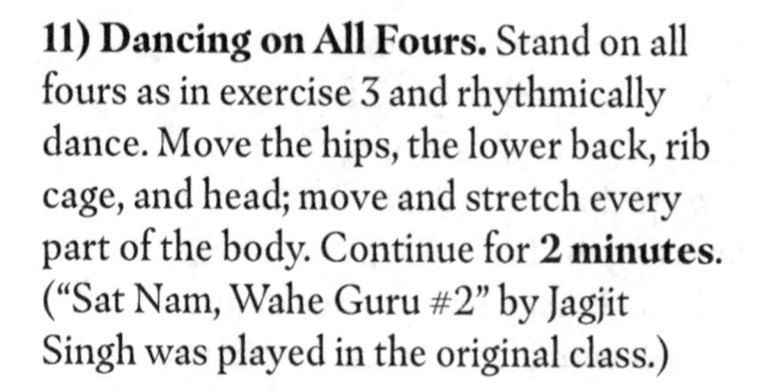

11) Dancing on All Fours. Stand on all fours as in exercise 3 and rhythmically dance. Move the hips, the lower back, rib cage, and head; move and stretch every part of the body. Continue for **2 minutes.** ("Sat Nam, Wahe Guru #2" by Jagjit Singh was played in the original class.)

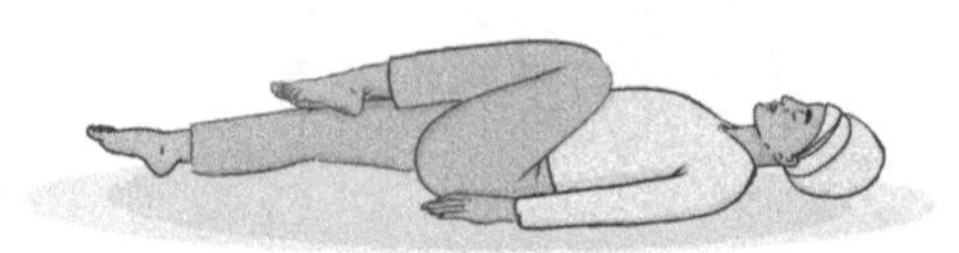

12) Push-Pull Legs. Lie on the back with the legs together and the hands at the sides palms on the ground. Raise the legs 1-½ inches (2-3 cm) feet off the ground. Alternately pull one knee to the chest while pushing the other leg out to the starting position, like a piston motion. The legs stay parallel to the ground, toes pointed. Continue for **1 ½ minutes.** ("Sat Nam, Wahe Guru #2" by Jagjit Singh was played in the original class.)

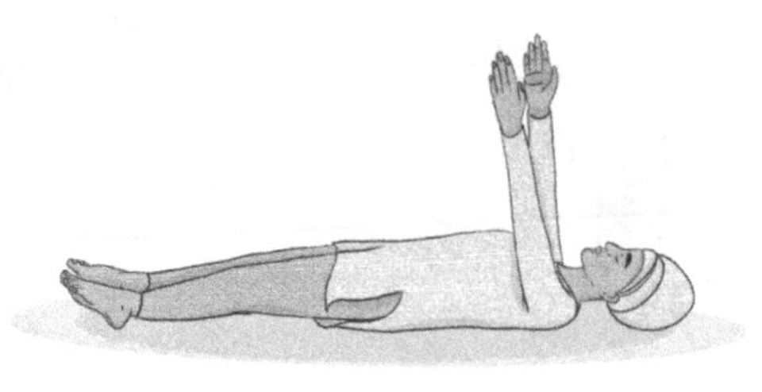

13) Arms Movement. Remain on the back, stretch the arms up straight and open wide. Move the arms toward each other with force, but stop before the hands touch, then return to starting position. Continue for **1 minute**. ("Sat Nam, Wahe Guru #2" by Jagjit Singh was played in the original class.) *This kriya exercises the muscles of the chest area.*

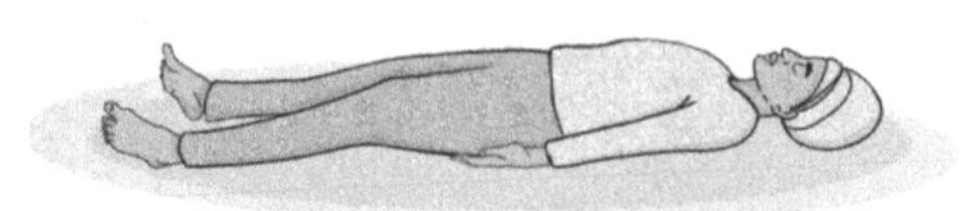

14) Relaxation. Remain on the back with the arms at the sides of the body, palms facing up, and totally relax and sleep. Project from your Third Eye Point. "Sat Nam, Wahe Guru #2", by Jagjit was played in the original class. After **9 minutes**, sing with the music for another

2 minutes. (Gong was played along with the music for the first 6 minutes.) TO END: Wake up. Roll the wrists and ankles, rub the hands and feet, roll on the back.

15) Tree Pose. Stand up with the feet hip width apart. Balance on one foot and place the sole of the other foot on the inside of the opposite leg, heel close to the groin, toes pointing down. Keep the eyes open and focus on a point straight ahead. Stretch the arms up above the head in Prayer Pose. The bent knee points out to the side. Hold for **45 seconds.** Switch legs and hold for **15 seconds.**

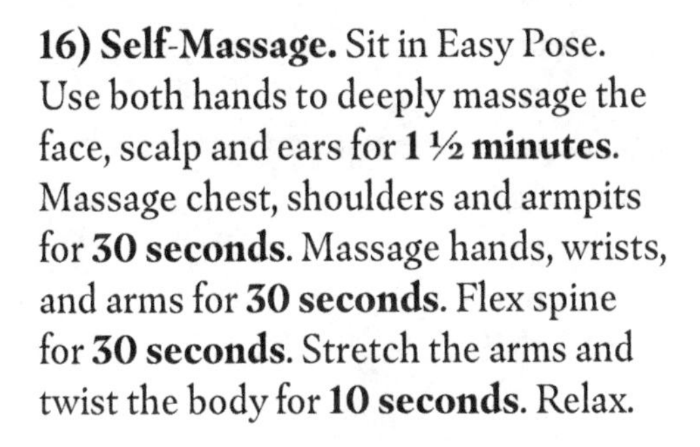

16) Self-Massage. Sit in Easy Pose. Use both hands to deeply massage the face, scalp and ears for **1 ½ minutes.** Massage chest, shoulders and armpits for **30 seconds**. Massage hands, wrists, and arms for **30 seconds**. Flex spine for **30 seconds.** Stretch the arms and twist the body for **10 seconds**. Relax.

Comments: Just before the spring season begins, practice this kriya every day for a week to renew the body after the winter.

TAKE ON ONLY AS MUCH AS YOU CAN ALSO LET GO

Is it easier for you to bring something into your life than it is to let go? If so, greater ease with inhaling versus exhaling might reflect this psychological trait on your physical level. Or is the opposite true in most life situations: Is it easier for you to remove something from your life than it is to invite it in? Then you might find greater ease with exhaling. You achieve a balance when both sides of your breath are equal and easy, and you only take in as much as you can also let go. This kriya helps you achieve that kind of balance in your breath and in your life. Praana represents the energy of inflow, and apaana the outflow, and both are just the same universal life force flowing in different directions. With a balance in praanic energy and your breath, your life never feels burdened and overwhelming, and never empty and starved.

BALANCING PRAANA AND APAANA

November 7, 1984

1) Balance the Body. Come onto the hands and knees, with the knees directly under the hips and the palms flat on the ground directly under the shoulders. Do not bend the elbows. Stretch the left leg straight back and the right arm straight forward with both leg and arm held parallel to the ground, creating a balanced posture. Hold the posture for **3 minutes**. Switch sides and raise the right leg and left arm to the same position as the other side. Hold the posture for **2 ½ minutes**. *This posture will balance the body and strengthen the apaanic (eliminating) energy.*

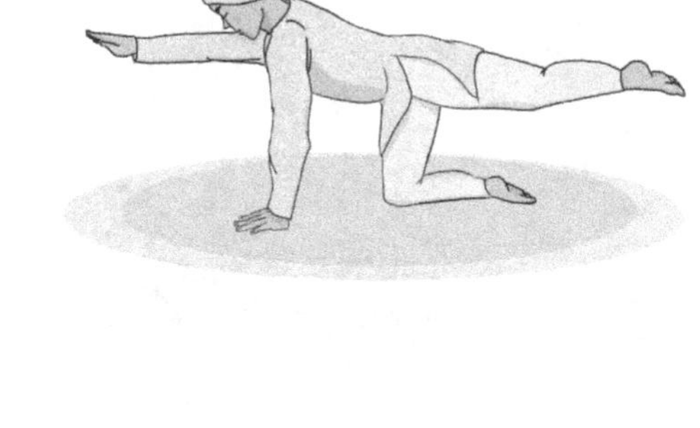

2) Kriya of Virtue. From Rock Pose, rise up to stand on your knees and stretch the arms straight up. Draw the navel in so that you can feel the tops of your feet pressing into the ground. Lift the chest and bend backward, keeping the navel engagement and stretching away from the lower back. Begin to move your arms, neck and head in large circles; your shoulders will move but your knees remain stable. Continue for **2 minutes**.

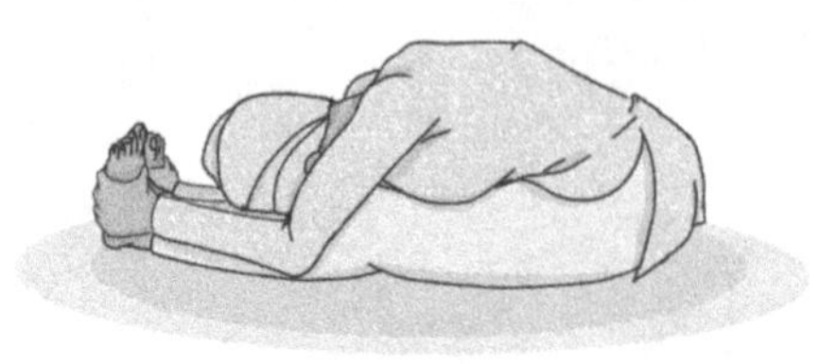

3) Life Nerve Stretch. Sit with the legs stretched forward, with a straight spine and a light Neck Lock. Elongate the spine as you bend from the hips, and grasp the soles of the feet; rest the upper body on your thighs and place the chin between the legs if possible. Concentrate at the Third Eye Point and hold the posture for **5 minutes**. (Gong was played in the original class for the last **2 ½ minutes.**)

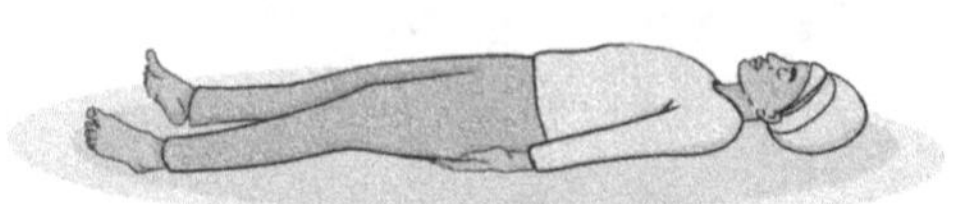

4) Relaxation. Lie on the back in Corpse Pose and deeply relax every part of your body while you project your energy out from the Third Eye Point. Continue for **6 minutes**. (Gong was played in the original class.)

Breath In, Breath Out
Keep Up With Your Journey

TUNE UP YOUR INNER WASTE DISPOSAL

Not only do you digest your food, you also digest your experiences, and negative experiences can affect your digestive system in ways similar to a diet of junk food. We get clogged up, sluggish, foggy, and depressed. If we understand that there is a symbiotic relationship between our internal physical and energetic processes, it's no wonder that the same organs that remove toxins from your body can also remove darkness from your life. These organs include the liver, colon, and stomach, and today's kriya supports all of them. With a healthy digestive system, you are much more likely to face a situation and say: "Yes, I can get through this, not a problem for me at all."

KRIYA FOR THE LIVER, COLON AND STOMACH

Originally published in Youth & Joy

1) Standing Bends. Stand up with a straight spine and a light Neck Lock, the legs a little wider than shoulder width apart. Place your hands on the hips. Bend from the waist and chant in the following sequence: to the right on **SAA**, to the left on **TAA**, forward on **NAA** and back on **MAA**, returning to the upright position after each movement. Move at a pace of 1 second in each direction. Continue rhythmically for **5 minutes**.
This exercise opens up the hip area and prepares you for the next exercise.

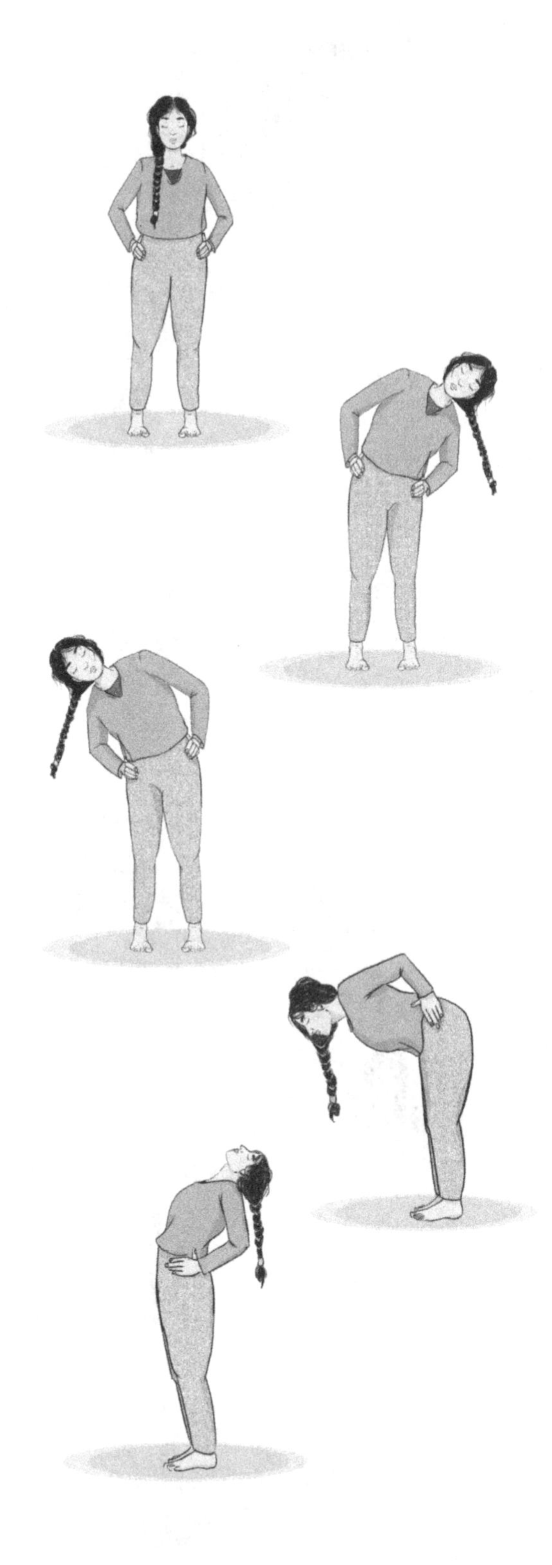

2) Standing Torso Circles. Remain standing with the legs a little wider than shoulder width apart and the hands on the hips. Rotate the torso in very large circles from the hips 1 rotation per second. Continue for **2-3 minutes**. Then begin chanting **HAR HARI** with each rotation and continue for **2 more minutes**.
This exercise stimulates the gonads.

3) Standing Bends Variation. Stand with the legs a little wider than hip width apart, and your arms relaxed down at your sides. Move and chant in the following sequence: grasp opposite upper arms and raise the arms parallel to the ground on **SAA**, lean backwards and raise the locked arms up and back on **TAA**, come back to standing with the locked arms parallel to the ground on **NAA**, and relax the arms down next to the body on **MAA**. Move rhythmically, 2-3 seconds per cycle. Continue for **3-4 minutes**.
This exercise relieves lower back pain and pressurizes the lymph glands.

4) Crow Pose Variation. Remain standing, legs are hip width apart with the arms parallel to the ground, grasping the upper arms. Move and chant in the following sequence: squat down into Crow Pose on **SAA**, come standing back up on **TAA**, squat down on **NAA**, and come standing back up on **MAA**. Move rhythmically, 3 seconds per complete cycle. Continue for **3 minutes.**
This exercise balances the body's energy. It also works to relieve pain in the lower back.

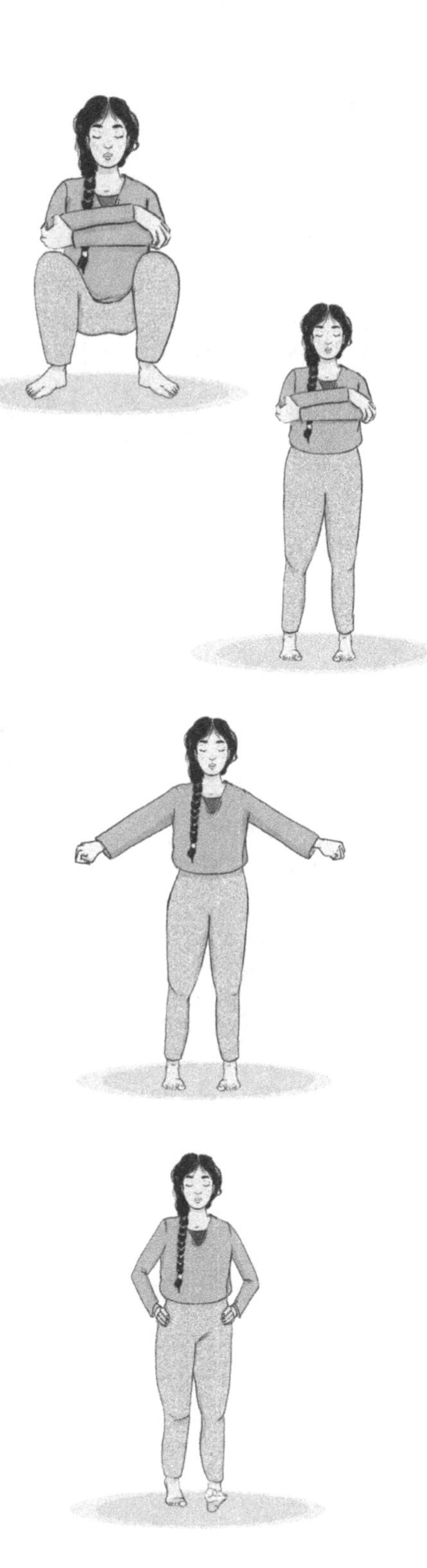

5) Arm Circles with Chanting.
Remain standing. Touch the thumbs to the fleshy mound at the base of the Mercury (little) fingers and make fists, folding the fingers over the thumbs. Rotate both arms backwards rapidly in large circles, moving from the shoulders. Chant the mantra: **HAR HAR HAR HAR HAR HAR HAREE** at a pace of 1 repetition per 2-3 circles. Continue rhythmically for **2-3 minutes**.
This exercise balances the psyche and *enhances communication skills.*

6) Yogic Kicks. Remain standing with the feet closer together and balance on the balls of the feet. Place the hands on the hips. Kick the feet forward alternately at a quick pace. Chant: **HUM DUM HAR HAR, HAR HAR HUM DUM**, 1 kick with each word every 3-4 seconds. Continue rhythmically for **3 minutes**. Immediately start the next exercise.
This exercise balances the minerals in the body.

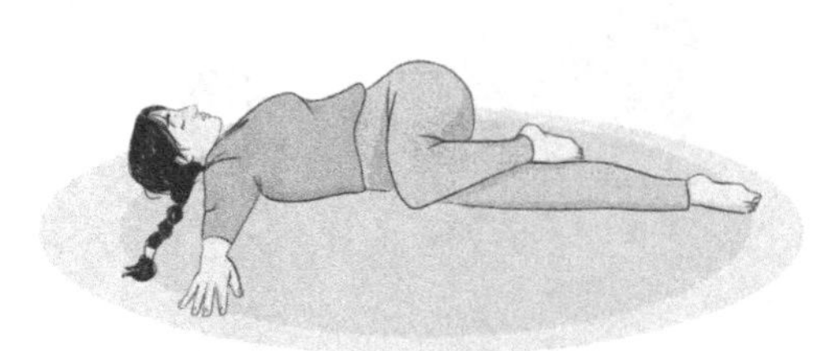

7) Cat Stretch. Lie on the back. Stretch the arms out to the sides with the palms facing up. Keeping the shoulders and arms on the ground, bend the right knee, take it as far as possible across the body to the left as you turn the head to the right, creating a gentle twist through the spine. The right knee ideally is on the ground at the side of the left knee. Bring the right knee and head back to center, and stretch the right leg straight forward on the ground. Repeat with the left leg. Alternate legs for **1-2 minutes**. *This exercise puts a pressure on the liver* and *removes toxins. It also consolidates the effects of the previous exercises.*

8) Sphinx Pose. Lie on the stomach with the arms at the sides and chin on the ground. Bring the elbows under the shoulders with the forearms and hands on the ground, parallel to each other. Press the forearms, pubic bone and legs into the ground and lift the head and chest up. Keep the elbows tucked into the sides. Draw the shoulder blades down, lift the Heart Center and draw the chin inwards towards the back of your neck. Kick the buttocks hard with alternate heels for **3-4 minutes** at a moderate pace. Kick rapidly for **1 more minute**. *This exercise is specifically for regulating the calcium/magnesium balance in the bloodstream and body which is controlled up the thigh bone. This bone also controls one's sexuality. The exercise applies a maximum pressure to the parathyroid and thyroid when the neck is up and the chin is out.*

9) Frog Pose with Chanting. Come into Frog Pose, squatting with the heels off the ground and the knees wide. The heels touch and fingertips are on the ground between the legs and close to the body. Keep the spine as straight as possible. Chant mentally and move in the following sequence: inhale and straighten the legs while raising the hips on **SAA**, exhale and return to Frog Pose on **TAA**, inhale and come back up on **NAA** and exhale and return to Frog Pose on **MAA**. Continue rhythmically, synchronizing the movement with the mantra for **5 minutes**. (1 cycle every 2-3 seconds.)
This exercise works on the knees.

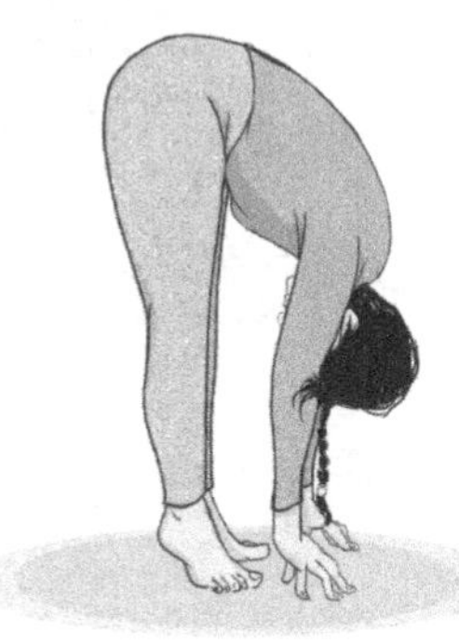

10) Sit and Stand. Stand up straight with the arms hanging loosely down by your sides, then sit down in a loose cross-legged position, ready to come standing up just as you reach the ground. Alternate the standing/sitting movement **4 times**.
This exercise balances the praana and apana in the body.

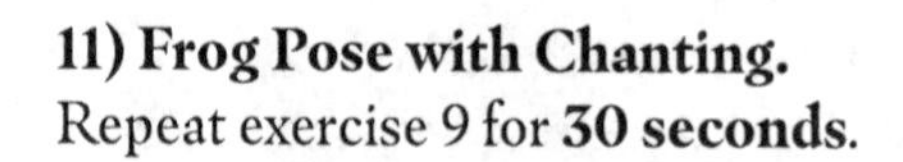

11) Frog Pose with Chanting.
Repeat exercise 9 for **30 seconds**.

12) Sitali Pranayam. Lie on the back, raise the legs and grasp the toes, keeping the legs straight. Curl the tongue into a "U" shape and extend it slightly past the lips. Inhale deeply through the curled tongue, exhale through the nose. Continue for **1-2 minutes.**
The breath used in this exercise cools the body.

13) Arm Flips. Sit in Easy Pose with a straight spine and a light Neck Lock. Place the arms in front of the body, parallel to the ground at shoulder level. The fingers point inwards with the fingertips meeting at the center of the chest, palms facing downwards. Starting with the left arm, straighten the arm out to the side with a quick jerk from the elbow, palm facing forward. Quickly return to the center starting position. Repeat with alternate arms for **3 minutes.**
This exercise works directly on the forearm muscle which regulates the colon.

14) Spinal Flex. Sit in Easy Pose with a straight spine and a Light Neck Lock. Grasp the knees firmly. Keeping the elbows straight, flex the upper spine forward and lift the chest on the inhale; flex the upper spine backward on the exhale. The movement is at the level of the upper thoracic spine in the heart area. The head is still and remains in Neck Lock. Continue at a moderate pace for **4 minutes**.
This exercise is for the lymph area. If done correctly it will create an unusual pressure behind the ears on the neck. It means your whole nervous system and central nervous system, the Shushumna, is stretching. It should create sweat on the face.

15) Fist Pumps. Remain in Easy Pose. Touch the thumbs to the fleshy mound at the base of the Mercury (little) fingers and make loose fists, folding the fingers over the thumbs. Place the fists at the side of the shoulders, elbows at the sides of the body. Stretch both arms up on the inhale, and lower the fists to the shoulders on the exhale. Move rapidly for **2-3 minutes**.
This exercise works on the spine and the sciatic nerve.

16) Neck Bends. Remain in Easy Pose. Raise the arms parallel to the ground and grasp opposite upper arms. Bend the neck and chant in the following sequence: to the right on **SAA**, back to center on **TAA**, to the left on **NAA**, and back to the center on **MAA**. (1 complete cycle every 2-3 seconds.) Continue rhythmically for **1-2 minutes**. *This exercise adjusts the neck.*

17) Meditate. Remain in Easy Pose and sing the song "Nobility" by Sangeet Kaur for **4 minutes**, or sit meditatively and breathe long and deep for **4 minutes**.

Breath In, Breath Out
Keep Up With Your Journey

A QUICK WAY TO GET YOUR JUICES FLOWING

If you enjoyed the effects of the Kriya for the Lymph System and want to keep the flow going in less time, a short refresher like the following kriya might be just the right thing. It only has three asanas, but is powerful enough to turn things around and make you feel like flowing downstream again. The set is yet another tool in our program to deliver the ease of unobstructed flow to your life, and variety in your toolbox is a splendid thing. It means you'll know just the right application for any life situation, no matter how much time or energy you find yourself with.

KRIYA TO REFRESH THE LYMPH SYSTEM

July 9, 1984

There are no breaks between exercises.

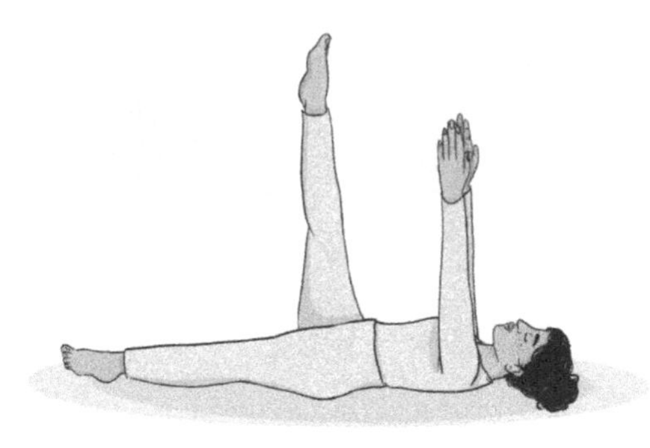

1) Arm Raises. Lie on the back with both legs actively engaged. Raise the right leg straight up to 90 degrees, keeping the left leg on the ground. Hold the legs steady and raise both arms up to 90 degrees and lower them back down to the sides of the body. The arms move very rapidly. Continue for **3 minutes.** Switch legs and continue for **3 minutes.** *This exercise moves the chest and stimulates the surrounding lymph area.*

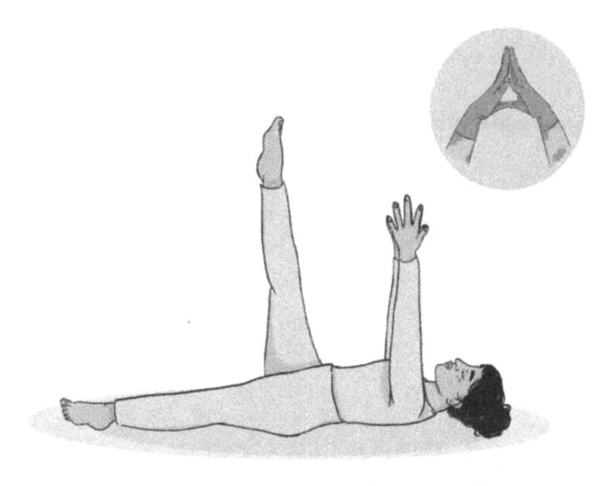

2) Alternate Leg Lifts Variation. Remain on the back and stretch the arms straight up perpendicular to the ground. Touch the fingertips of corresponding fingers and rotate the fingers in circles; the palms will move towards and then away from each other. At the same time, slowly raise and lower alternate legs to 90 degrees. Continue for **8 minutes.** *The tips of the fingers relate to specific areas in the brain. Rotating the fingers this way is like massaging the brain.*

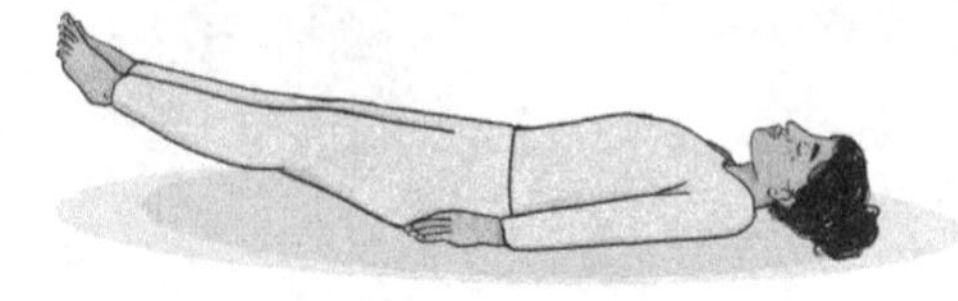

3) Knees Strike Chest. Remain on the back and extend the legs out to 60 degrees. Powerfully pull both knees into the chest and stretch them back out. Ideally the knees hit the body. Move rapidly for **3 minutes**. *This movement brings circulation to the breast area.*

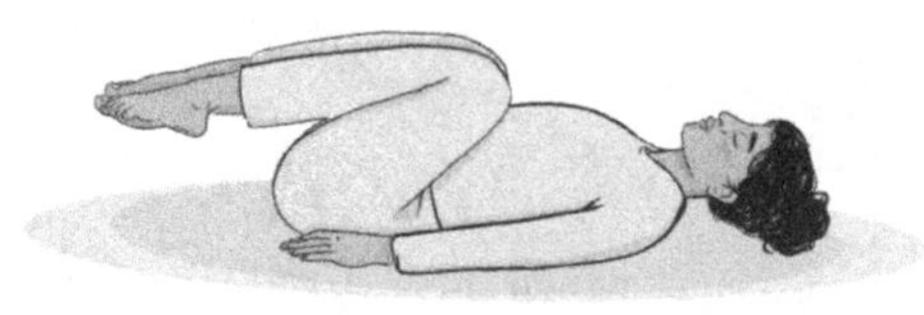

4) Relaxation. Remain on the back and inhale and exhale through pursed lips (like a soft whistle), relax the body and sleep. Continue for **11-62 minutes**.

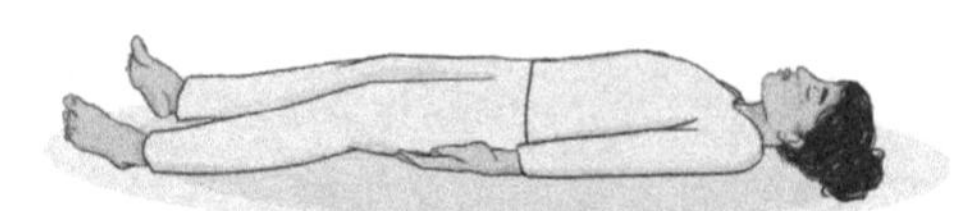

Breath In, Breath Out
Keep Up With Your Journey

OPEN YOUR WINDOWS FOR A FRESH BREEZE

Consider these two ways of dealing with a problem: You could hold up all of its pieces and shower them with your thoughts and attention, keeping them and the entire problem alive. Or you could drop each piece until all of them are gone and the problem simply disappears. Think of this kriya as the energetic equivalent to the latter approach. The idea is to get rid of clutter that weighs you down and to find newness and health in the empty space that opens up. It makes sense for everyone's life, but especially for the stubborn clutter that accumulates from the effects of sexual violence. Moreover, this short kriya is a wonderful meditative experience, like a sheet hanging on a clothesline being dried by sunshine and warm air until its natural lightness and elasticity are restored.

KRIYA FOR PURIFYING THE SELF

Originally published in Sadhana Guidelines

1) Standing Lunge Stretch. Stand and extend one leg back as far as possible with the top of the foot on the ground. Bend the opposite knee until the thigh is almost parallel with the ground, keeping the knee above the ankle. Most of the weight is on the front leg. Place the palms together in Prayer Pose at the center of the chest, keep the spine elongated with a light Neck Lock and focus at the Third Eye Point. Inhale deeply, suspend the breath for **8 seconds** and exhale. Repeat for **2 more breaths.** Switch legs and inhale deeply, suspend the breath for **8 seconds**, exhale and repeat for **2 more breaths**. Repeat the entire sequence **2 more times** in each position.

2) Pranayam. Sit in Easy Pose with a straight spine and a light Neck Lock. Place the hands on the hips. Lift the diaphragm and raise both shoulders as high as possible. Breathe slow complete breaths. Continue for **2-3 minutes.**
This exercise takes energy past the diaphragm lock and opens the lungs and throat chakra.

3) Bear Grip Variation. Remain in Easy Pose. Bring the hands in front of the Heart Center with the right palm facing down and the left facing up; curl the right fingers into the left in Bear Grip. Keep the forearms parallel to the ground. Inhale deeply, exhale forcefully and completely, suspend the breath and apply Root Lock. Inhale, suspend the breath, apply Root Lock and mentally raise the energy from the base of the spine to the crown. Continue the entire breath sequence for **3 minutes**.
This exercise opens the heart and the central channel of the spine.

4) Arms to the Sides. Remain in Easy Pose. Extend the arms out to the sides, parallel to the ground. Bend the wrists and press the palms outward, fingers pointing up. Focus at the Third Eye Point. Inhale deeply, suspend the breath for **20 seconds** and apply Root Lock, exhale. Continue this breath cycle for **2-3 minutes**.

5) Prayer Pose Variation. Remain in Easy Pose. Press the palms together in Prayer Pose, held 2-3 inches (5-8 cm) in front of the chest. Apply steady strong pressure on the hands. Continue for **2 minutes**.

Comments: This kriya guides energy along the spine, opening the chakras and expanding the aura. It energizes you and helps purify the mind and body. It is an excellent preparation before giving a massage or healing treatment.

Breath In, Breath Out
Keep Up With Your Journey

BOOST YOUR MOODS AND BRAIN POWER

Depression, fatigue, and memory loss can be related to parathyroid function, so a well-functioning parathyroid can elevate your mood, your thoughts, and your level of energy. This kriya helps optimize your parathyroid and brain so that you can be in a great psychological and physical state. It only has three asanas, but each is intense in its own way, so let each one be a trip into the wonderland of your consciousness. A blissful ending is guaranteed with the final piece, a moving meditation that spins you into a state of ecstasy.

KRIYA FOR THE BRAIN AND PARATHYROID

Originally published in Youth & Joy

1) Spinal Twist with Chanting. Sit in Easy Pose with a straight spine and a light Neck Lock. Interlock the hands behind the head at the hairline (under any loose hair) and twist the body powerfully from left to right. Keep the elbows stretched to the sides. Move rapidly, chanting 1 repetition every 2-3 seconds: **HARI HAR, HARI HAR, HARI HAR, HARI** with the tip of the tongue hitting the upper palate behind the teeth. Rhythmically coordinate the movement with the mantra. Continue for **4 minutes**. *This exercise stimulates the thyroid and parathyroid glands.*

2) Bowing Jaap Sahib. Sit between the heels with the buttocks touching the ground in Celibate Pose. Keep the spine straight with a light Neck Lock. Interlock the hands behind the head at the hairline (under any loose hair). Listen to the recording of Jaap Sahib, sit meditatively for the first stanza and bend from the hips touching the forehead to the ground every time you hear Namastang or Namo. Without the recording, the movement is done to 10 beats as follows: Bow down and come up in 2 beats for 4 cycles, and rest in the starting position, on beats 9 and 10. Continue for **15 minutes**. *This exercise works on the pituitary and parathyroid glands and reproductive system.*

3) Torso Circle Variation. Sit in Easy Pose with a straight spine and a light Neck Lock. Place the palms on the ground at the sides of the body with the elbows straight. Rotate the body in large circles, moving from the hips and the power of the navel. Chant **WHAA-HAY GUROO WHAA-HAY GUROO, WHAA-HAY GUROO, WHAA-HAY JEEO**. Rhythmically coordinate the movement with the mantra. Continue for **15 minutes.** *This exercise works on the parathyroid gland and develops the power to listen.*

Breath In, Breath Out
Keep Up With Your Journey

CHANGE YOUR GAME

There's a good chance that you've never had an experience quite like Gyan Chakra Meditation. Even for experienced Kundalini yogis, this meditation is in a league of its own for feeling that anything is possible — which is why we are including it in our program. Yes, you'll be moving your arms above your head for eleven minutes, but the rewards are manifold as you magnetize your aura for great health and prosperity. If sexual violence has given you a sense of stagnation, the feeling that life can never be entirely burden-free again, try this kriya and stick with it for a while, then see what it does for your perspective. Just contemplate this gem from the original notes about this meditation for a moment: "Your capacity to realize change changes."

GYAN CHAKRA KRIYA MEDITATION

February 19, 1996

Sit in Easy Pose with a straight spine and a light Neck Lock.

Mudra: Place the hands in Gyan Mudra, touch the tip of the thumbs with the Jupiter (index) fingers and keep the other three fingers extended. With the elbows bent and arms curved, circle one hand inward starting in front of the body no lower than the Heart Center, moving back and up to the opposite side of the head, back around the head, returning in front of the body. The hands move continuously in an inward circle with the palms facing outward. Alternate the arms, so that as the one arm comes over the head, the other arm is circling out to the side of the body, like a rapid whirling motion around the head (1 revolution per second.)

Eye Focus: Not specified.

Breath: Not specified.

Mantra: Chant powerfully from the Navel Point. ("Sat Nam, Wahe Guru #2", by Jagjit Singh was played in the original class).

SAT NAAM SAT NAAM, WHAA-HAY GUROO WHAA-HAY GUROO

Time: 11 minutes.

To End: Speed up the movement for the last **10 seconds**. Inhale deeply, suspend the breath, and stretch the arms straight over the head hugging the ears, hold for **10 seconds** and exhale. Repeat one more time. Inhale deeply, suspend the breath, keep the arms up, twist left and right for 7 cycles, exhale.

Comments: This meditation is fantastic for healing. It helps the heart and joints, decreases stored anger and increases intuition. It also expands the arcline, so that opportunities naturally come to you. Begin with 11 minutes daily for 40 days. Then increase to 11 minutes twice a day for 40 days.

Breath In, Breath Out
Keep Up With Your Journey

TAP THE BEST SOURCE FOR LOVE

The day that you realize you can give yourself the love that you've been looking for on the outside is the day that everything changes. You may have already gained this wisdom in your lifetime, and it certainly has found its way into pop culture as there is no shortage of versions of the same idea all around us: "You gotta love yourself to love others". It's almost cliche, but it's also the absolute truth. The thing about such profound wisdom is that no matter how often you hear it, you still forget it, and we all go back to looking for love in all the wrong places first, i.e. outside of ourselves. But not today. Today's practice is all about the one thing you never have to run out of because you can create it yourself — infinite love of the self.

CREATING SELF-LOVE

April 4, 1994

PART ONE

Sit in Easy Pose with a straight spine and a light Neck Lock.

Mudra: Place the right hand 6-9 inches (15-23 cm) above the top of the head, with the fingers together and palm facing the down. Bend the left elbow and place the forearm next to the rib cage with the hand facing forward and fingers together.

Eye Focus: Closed and focused on the Moon Center at the tip of the chin.

Breath: Long Deep Breathing with one minute breath cycle (inhale 20 seconds, suspend the breath 20 seconds, and exhale 20 seconds).

Time: 11 minutes.

To End: Inhale deeply and immediately begin Part Two.

PART TWO

Remain in Easy Pose.

Mudra: Extend the arms straight forward, parallel to the ground, palms facing down. Actively stretch to your maximum.

Eye Focus: Closed and focused on the Moon Center at the tip of the chin.

Breath: Long Deep Breathing.

Time: 3 minutes.

To End: Inhale deeply and immediately begin Part Three.

PART THREE

Remain in Easy Pose with a firm Neck Lock.

Mudra: Stretch the arms up straight with the palms facing forward, keeping the upward stretch throughout the exercise. There is no bend in the elbows.

Eye Focus: Closed and focused on the Moon Center at the tip of the chin.

Breath: Long Deep Breathing.

Time: 3 minutes.

To End: Inhale, suspend the breath for **10 seconds** and stretch the arms and fingers straight up (stretch so much that the buttocks lift) and tighten all the muscles of the body. Exhale. Repeat **2 more** times.

Comments: The first exercise, Reverse Adi Shakti Kriya, is a mental hypnotic self-blessing that adjusts the aura and magnetic field. The left palm faces forward and blesses the world. The second exercise benefits the upper body from the navel to the neck. It strengthens the heart and opens the Heart Center as love blossoms and fear is reduced.

BUILD AN ENERGETIC SHIELD OF PROTECTION

In yogic anatomy, there is the concept of an energy field around us that gives protection and guidance. It is called the arcline, and practicing this kriya develops this field and its benefits: a greater sense that the world is a safe place and that the universe supports you. From this safe place, you can trust more, especially the guidance from your own intuition. The good listening skills you need to engage with your intuition become well-sharpened in this kriya as you listen carefully to your own breath and voice.

KRIYA TO EXPAND THE ARCLINE

April 10, 1996

PART ONE

Sit in Easy Pose with a straight spine and a light Neck Lock.

Mudra: Make fists with the Jupiter (index) and Saturn (middle) fingers extended, and the other fingers held down with the thumbs. Raise the hands to the level of the ears with the forearms perpendicular to the ground and palms facing forward. Elbows are at the sides.

Eye Focus: Closed.

Breath: Inhale and exhale through an "O" shaped mouth.

Mental Focus: Concentrate on and listen to the sound of the breath.

Time: Continue for **8 minutes** and immediately begin Part Two.

PART TWO

Remain in Easy Pose.

Mudra: Maintain the mudra in Part One.

Eye Focus: Closed.

Mantra: Chant **HAR** from the navel, pulling in the navel and touching the tongue to the upper palate with each repetition.

Time: 4 minutes.

To End: Inhale deeply, suspend the breath for **10 seconds**, tighten the lips, concentrate on the Navel Point, and visualize a line of energy in the body. Cannon Fire exhale. Repeat **1 more time**. Relax and talk to each other for a few minutes. (If practicing alone, talk to yourself for a few minutes).

Breath In, Breath Out
Keep Up With Your Journey

FEEL ALIVE

You spend so much time thinking and planning and working and doing — most of it in the hope that your life and your feelings will improve. Take time today to acknowledge how good things already are, and try this kriya to find out how easily you can make yourself feel good, even if you have desires that are still unfilled. Feeling alive is possible every day, and taking a break to do it consciously is a good idea for your well-being, so you won't spend your entire waking life – like most people – in anticipation of a better future. This kriya connects you to yourself and to others and invites you to feel joyful in your own skin. It ends with chest beating, like King Kong does in movies, which everyone easily understands as a declaration of power. It's no different here; show the world and yourself the power of your vitality, the fact that you are alive — and that's enough.

MEDITATION FOR VITALITY

July 10, 1998

PART ONE

Sit in Easy Pose with a straight spine and a light Neck Lock.

Mudra: Bend the elbows and bring the hands in line with the ears, wrists at the level of the shoulders and forearms perpendicular to the ground. Elbows are at the sides. Place the hands in Ravi Mudra, touch the tips of the thumb and Sun (ring) fingers and extend the other fingers straight up with the palms facing forward.

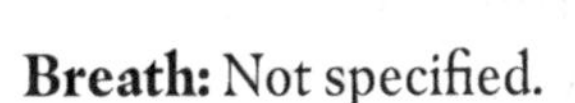

Breath: Not specified.

Eye Focus: Closed.

Mantra: Chant the Kundalini Bhakti Mantra for **31 minutes**. (The version by Gurudass Kaur was played in the original class.)

AADEE SHAKTEE, AADEE SHAKTEE, AADEE SHAKTEE, NAMO, NAMO

SARAB SHAKTEE, SARAB SHAKTEE, SARAB SHAKTEE, NAMO, NAMO

PRITHAM BHAGVATEE, PRITHAM BHAGVATEE, PRITHAM BHAGVATEE, NAMO, NAMO

KUNDALINEE MAATAA SHAKTEE, MAATAA SHAKTEE, NAMO, NAMO

To End: Inhale, keep the posture steady, and move immediately into Part Two.

PART TWO

Mudra & Mantra: Keep the same mudra. Chant **HAR**, pulling in the Navel Point with each recitation. Continue for **4 more minutes**. ("Tantric Har" version by Simran Kaur was played in the original class.)

Total Time: 35 minutes.

To End: Inhale deeply, suspend the breath for **15-20 seconds**, and exhale with a whistle. Repeat **1 more time**. Inhale deeply, suspend the breath for **10-15 seconds**, squeeze the body, and Cannon Fire exhale. Relax.

Breath In, Breath Out
Keep Up With Your Journey

LIVE THE BIG PICTURE

All yoga is about your connection to the universal consciousness, and this kriya takes that concept and makes it specific in relation to the psyche. The idea is that the feeling of true harmony can only exist if not just your own psyche is balanced, but if your unit psyche is balanced with the psyche of your environment plus the psyche of the whole landscape. Sounds like an insurmountable task? Not at all, it's just a matter of tuning yourself in and feeling and seeing the big picture. For example, you are at home in the evening, your hometown is quieting down, and the moon comes up above the whole landscape. There is a sum feeling to all of this, a particular flavor of day's end, the psyche of all of it together with you inside of it. But if at that moment you only think nervously about the next day and some challenge that awaits you then, you are out of tune with the calmer evening mood of your whole surroundings. This could be one reason why you feel alone and lacking support. Return to harmony with this kriya and understand the blessings of being in sync with your world. With that expanded consciousness, the universe always has your back.

KRIYA BALANCING THE THREE PSYCHES

May 24, 1984

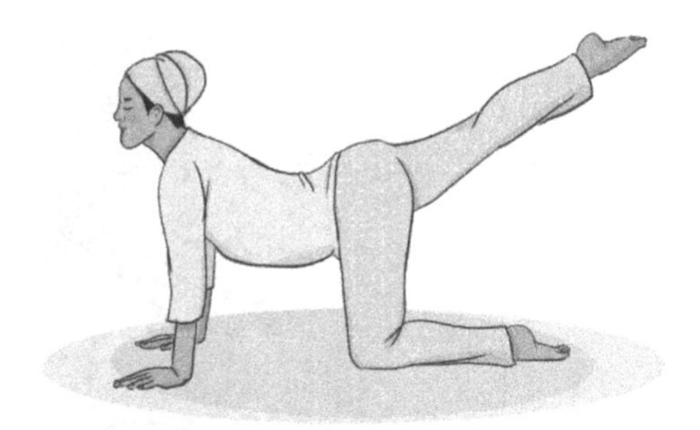

1) Cow Pose Foot Flexing. Come onto your hands and knees in Cow Pose, with knees directly under the hips and arms straight, palms flat on the ground directly under the shoulders. Arch the spine downward, lowering the abdomen and lifting the sternum and chin. Extend the left leg back and raise it to 60 degrees. Point and flex the left foot, in rhythm with a powerful Breath of Fire. Continue for **3 minutes.** Switch legs and continue for **1 ½ minutes.**

2) Cat Pose Punching. Come onto your hands and knees in Cat Pose, with knees directly under the hips and arms straight, palms flat on the ground directly under the shoulders. Round the spine up toward the ceiling and bring the chin toward the chest. Make a fist of your left hand in front of your Heart Center and begin punching forward in rhythm with Breath of Fire. Punch strongly, so that the shoulder blades move. Continue for **2 minutes.** Switch arms and continue for **1 ½ minutes.**

3) Bow and Clap. Sit on the heels in Rock Pose with a straight spine and a light Neck Lock. Bend from the hips touching the forehead to the ground and simultaneously stretch the arms behind you and clap the hands behind the back. Rise back up. Continue for **3 ½ minutes**.

4) Wrist Flexes. Sit in Easy Pose with a straight spine and a light Neck Lock. Stretch the arms straight forward parallel to the ground with the palms facing down. Touch the thumbs at the base of the Mercury (little) fingers and keep the other fingers straight. Flex the hands down and back rapidly 8 times (2 seconds per complete cycle). After the 8th flex, rapidly pull the arms back with the elbows on the rib cage, forearms perpendicular to the ground, hands facing forward and fingers pointing up. Continue for **1 ½ minutes**.

5) Relaxation. Lie down on the back in Corpse Pose and relax for **5-11 minutes**.

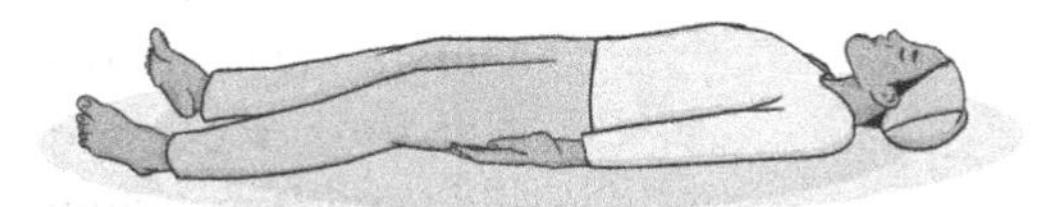

Comments: In yogic philosophy there are three psyches: your individual inner psyche, the psyche which is in your immediate environment, and the psyche of the landscape which is vaster. When these three psyches are in balance, you are in harmony.

TIME TO INVITE PEOPLE INTO YOUR LIFE

Almost every aspect of experiencing sexual violence leads to isolation — the pain and fear, the secrecy and confrontation, the living with the wounds. Isolation is a form of poverty, just like human connection is a form of wealth. This kriya develops your capacity to build the wealth of human connection by making it easy and efficient for you to meet people wherever they are so that you can join together. That is true prosperity, and it takes a certain attitude and projection. If sexual violence has isolated you, try this kriya and make your relationships mutually positive again.

LOVE YOURSELF AND LIVE AS YOURSELF

December 17, 1999

There are no breaks between the exercises.

1) Toss a Ball of Energy. Sit in Easy Pose with a straight spine and a light Neck Lock. Place the left hand on the Heart Center with fingers together pointing to the right and the thumb apart and relaxed. Place the right elbow at the side with the forearm forward parallel to the ground and the hand slightly cupped facing inward. In a quick fluid motion, flip the hand palm up and raise it up to the level of the Heart Center as if you are lightly tossing a ball of energy up to the sky. Immediately return to the starting position. Continue for **11 minutes.**
The gesture in this exercise is simple body language for 'what do I care?' The exercise will bring you energy, as you break through your doubts, change your arcline, and manifest the radiance of your true essence.

2) One Arm Raised. Remain in Easy Pose with the left hand on the Heart Center. Stretch the right arm straight up with the hand facing forward and fingers pointing up. Hold for **2 ½ minutes.**
Allow the breath to adjust and become a healing breath.

3) Arm Forward. Remain in Easy Pose. Stretch the left arm forward parallel to the ground with the hand facing down. Place the right hand behind the neck, beneath any loose hair, the right elbow stretched to the side and upper arm parallel to the ground. Hold with Breath of Fire for **1 ½ minutes**.

4) Meditate with Siri Gaitri Mantra. Remain in Easy Pose and place the hands in Prayer Pose at the Heart Center. Listen to the Siri Gaitri Mantra: **RAA MAA DAA SAA, SAA SAY SO HUNG** for **3 minutes**. Whisper the mantra for **1 ½ more minutes**, and chant the mantra for the last **3 minutes**.

5) Meditate Holding Hands. Remain in Easy Pose. Hold hands with people around you. (If practicing alone, imagine that you are holding hands with people). Continue to chant the Siri Gaitri Mantra for the first **3 minutes**. Then begin Long Deep Breathing for **2 minutes**. End chanting the Siri Gaitri Mantra for **1 ½ more minutes**. TO END: Inhale deeply, suspend the breath for **10 seconds**, exhale. Repeat **2 more times**, suspending the last breath for **15 seconds**.

Breath In, Breath Out

Keep Up With Your Journey

GET MORE ARCLINE POWER

The guidance and protection you get from your arcline is something that serves you everywhere you go, whether you're with others or alone. That is why we are adding more arcline tools, and today's kriya builds your arcline in yet another way. This one is challenging and requires your stamina — but awakening it may be just what you need.

Kundalini Yoga has many tools for building the arcline, as it usually offers more than one tool for just about any goal or solution. That is one reason why there are thousands of kriyas in Kundalini Yoga. The sheer number of tools may be overwhelming if you are new to the practice, but in time you'll appreciate that having multiple means to the same end gives you these two advantages: 1. Variety: Just like you can build a house with several materials, you can develop great health and wealth in one area of your practice by using multiple kriyas, e.g. for your arcline. 2. Expertise: When you try each of the different approaches once or a few times, you'll know what is available. And when the time comes to apply one, you'll know exactly which one to pick, just like a master chef will know exactly which ingredients make the most delicious meal.

KRIYA TO BUILD AN ARCLINE AURA

October 17, 1995

PART ONE

Sit in Easy Pose with a straight spine and a light Neck Lock.

Mudra: Raise the arms to form an arc over the head with the palms facing down. Touch the tips of the Mercury (little) fingers and let the other fingers naturally fit in the space between the corresponding fingers of the opposite hand. The thumbs are relaxed and not touching.

Eye Focus: Closed.

Breath: Slow, complete, Long Deep Breathing.

Time: 19 minutes.

PART TWO

Remain in Easy Pose, with eyes closed, breathing slowly and completely. Place the hands at the Heart Center.

Time: 20 minutes.

To End: Inhale deeply, suspend the breath for **15 seconds** and squeeze the rib cage, exhale powerfully. Repeat **1 more time**. Inhale deeply, suspend the breath for

20 seconds, stretch the arms up with fingers open, squeeze the body, exhale.

Comments: Because this position is challenging and the duration of the kriya is so long, "Tank of Harimandir" by Livtar Singh was played in the original class to help the class keep up through the exercise.

Breath In, Breath Out
Keep Up With Your Journey

AN EASY BREATH TO MAKE EVERYTHING BETTER

One of the most stubborn beliefs in humankind is this: Nothing good will come without some pain. It's also a false premise, and this kriya is one way to prove it wrong, because you can get major results just by breathing and moving your hands in an easy fashion for eleven minutes. So take it easy today without interrupting the flow of benefits that come from your daily practice. Today's benefits include: A disease-free body, a productive mind, a stronger immune system, great intuition, and just a better life all around.

THE BREATH OF TEN

May 8, 1995

Sit in Easy Pose with a straight spine and a light Neck Lock.

Mudra: Relax the elbows at the sides of the body. Extend the forearms forward just wider than the shoulders with relaxed hands facing each other. Move the hands in and out as if clapping, and stop before the hands come together (about 8 inches or 20 cm). Move rhythmically with the breath.

Eye Focus: Not specified.

Breath: Inhale in 5 strokes through the nose, exhale in 5 strokes through the mouth. Maintain a constant rhythm, 1 clapping motion on each stroke of the breath. The complete 10 stroke breath takes about **8 seconds**.

Mental Focus: Concentrate on the energy between the palms.

Time: 11 minutes.

To End: Inhale deeply, suspend the breath for **20 seconds**, place the hands on the face and press firmly, exhale. Inhale deeply, suspend the breath for **20 seconds**, place the hands on the Heart Center and press firmly, exhale. Inhale deeply, suspend the breath for **20 seconds**, place the hands on the Navel Point and press back firmly, exhale and relax.

APPLY THE SUPERPOWER OF COMPASSION

Most people think of compassion as a generous act of selflessness towards others. If you look at compassion through the self-focused lense of yogic teaching, all the benefits that others receive when you add compassion are returned manifold to you – the mental expansion from understanding someone else, the bigger heart from including them in your love, and the new softness that starts radiating from any situation immediately. Is self-gain enough reason to give compassion, you ask? Absolutely, especially when things have been hard and you need to heal. And don't forget the wonderful paradox of yoga: it's a self-centered practice that benefits everyone.

Yet another reason to try this kriya: The long mantra it uses, "Rakhay Rakhanaar". Master it and feel the satisfaction of knowing it by heart.

COMPASSION KRIYA

July 11, 1986

Sit in Easy Pose with a straight spine and a light Neck Lock.

Mudra: For both hands, cross the Saturn (middle) fingers over the Jupiter (index) fingers, keeping the Sun (ring) and Mercury (little) fingers straight. Place the thumbs on the mounds at the base of the Mercury (little) fingers. Press the hands on the Heart Center, left palm over right in position 1, and rest the wrists on the knees in position 2.

Eye Focus: Closed.

Breath: Not specified.

Mantra: Chant the mantra and synchronize the movement in the following sequence:

Position 1 on **RAKHAY RAKHANHAAR AAP UBAARIUN**

Position 2 on **GUR KEE PAIREE PAA-EH KAAJ SAVARIUN**

Position 1 on **HOAA AAP DAYAAL MANHO NA VISAARIUN**

Position 2 on **SAADH JANAA KAI SUNG BHAVJAL TAARIUN**

Position 1 on **SAAKAT NINDAK DUSHT KHIN MAA-EH BIDAARIUN**

Position 2 on **TIS SAAHIB KEE TAYK NAANAK MANAI MAA-EH**

Position 1 on **JIS SIMRAT SUKH HO-EH SAGLAY DOOKH JAA-EH**

Position 1 on **JIS SIMRAT SUKH HO-EH SAGLAY DOOKH JAA-EH**

Briefly lower the hands to Position 2 and continue the movement.

(Musical version by Singh Kaur was played in the original class.)

Time: 31 minutes.

Breath In, Breath Out
Keep Up With Your Journey

SOLIDIFY YOUR SHIELD

It's your third practice for the arcline, and three is the magic number here to make sure there will be no wobbling in your energetic field, just like you don't want to sit on a one or two-legged chair. Solidify the shield of protection and guidance, it'll be one of your best new friends.

MEDITATION FOR THE ARCLINE – REALIZE YOUR POWER

July 3, 1996

PART ONE

Sit in Easy Pose with a straight spine and a light Neck Lock.

Mudra: Make fists with the Jupiter (index) and Saturn (middle) fingers extended and the other fingers held down with the thumbs. With the elbows into the sides of the body, raise the forearms forward and up 45 degrees and rotate them out to the sides wider than the shoulders with hands facing forward. Move the forearms in touching the tips of Jupiter and Saturn fingers in front of the chest and return to the starting position. It's a continuous movement with no breaks between the hands' positions.

Eye Focus: Tip of the Nose.

Breath: Not specified.

Mantra: Chant **HAR** when the fingertips touch. ("Rhythms of Gatka", by Matamandir Singh was played in the original class.)

Time: 14 minutes.

PART TWO

Remain in Easy Pose.

Mudra and Mental Focus: Maintain the hand mudra and stretch the right arm up with the fingers pointing straight up and the palm facing forward. Place the left hand in front of the Heart Center, parallel to the ground, palm facing down and fingers pointing towards the right. Listen to the "Rhythms of Gatka" by Matamandir Singh and visualize the hands moving as in Part One. Just move mentally. Become completely still.

Eye Focus: Closed.

Time: 2 minutes.

Breath In, Breath Out

Keep Up With Your Journey

DISSOLVE YOUR PAST AT THE HEART

Kirtan Kriya is one of the most popular meditations in Kundalini Yoga and has been the subject of scientific studies. It's hard to find a Kundalini Yogi who doesn't know and love this gentle powerhouse, and if today is your first time practicing it, you're in for a treat. This is a version where your wrists are crossed at the heart level. The mantra is primal, almost like baby talk, and your fingers move along playfully and easily. And just like interacting with a baby can totally disarm you, the innocence of this kriya melts hardness and pain right around your heart. It is said to eliminate insecurities and allow your past to be processed and released.

CROSS HEART KIRTAN KRIYA MEDITATION

Originally published in The Mind

Sit in Easy Pose with a straight spine and a light Neck Lock.

Mudra: Cross the forearms below the wrists and hold them in front of the chest. The upper arms are on the rib cage, the forearms angled a little out and the palms are up and angled a little toward the body. Chant the Panj Shabad mantra and touch the tip of the thumb to the tip of each finger in the following sequence: thumb tip to the Jupiter (index) finger on **SAA**, thumb tip Saturn (middle) finger on **TAA**, thumb tip to Sun (ring) finger on **NAA** and thumb tip to Mercury (little) finger on **MAA**.

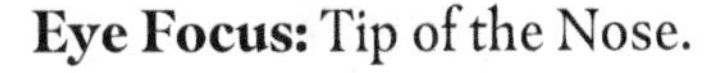

Eye Focus: Tip of the Nose.

Breath: Not specified.

Mantra: Chant **SAA TAA NAA MAA**.

Time: 11-31 minutes.

To End: Inhale deeply, suspend the breath, roll the eyes up, become completely still, exhale.

Comments: This meditation works on balancing the hemispheres of the brain, and helps to process past experiences and insecurities.

MANAGE ANGER AND NEGATIVITY WITH MEDITATION

There's a place and time for everything, and even anger and negativity, when applied with high consciousness and the right intention, can be very useful. Most of our anger and negativity, however, is reactionary and habitual and cuts us off from alignment with our higher self. In other words, in times when anger and negativity are the dominating emotions, it's not a good idea to talk with people, make decisions, or expect positive outcomes from just about any connected action. That's when it makes most sense to manage your emotions first, get back to a baseline of neutrality, and take a deep breath before you take action. This meditation is a helpful preparation like that.

MEDITATION TO WIPE OUT MENTAL NEGATIVITY

June 15, 1982

Sit in Easy Pose with a straight spine and a light Neck Lock.

Mudra: Relax the hands in the lap, palms face up with the right hand resting in the left. The tips of the thumbs touch.

Eye Focus: Closed.

Breath & Mantra: Inhale deeply. Chant the mantra **8 times** on each breath in a monotone. Pronounce each syllable distinctly. Breathe in very deeply in order to be able to chant the mantra 8 times on each breath.

WHAA-HAY GUROO, WHAA-HAY GUROO, WHAA-HAY GUROO, WHAA-HAY JEEO

Time: Begin with **11 minutes** and slowly build to **22 minutes** and then to **33 minutes**. Ultimately you can build the practice to **2 ½ hours**.

Comments: This mantra means, "You are beloved of my soul, Oh God." It causes a very subtle rub against the center of the palate, relaxing you. It brings mental clarity and you begin to experience the power of your soul, that tender light within you.

TOSS OUT MISFORTUNE LIKE OLD BATHWATER

This moving meditation looks like you are scooping up water in your palms, then tossing it behind you over your head. In this analogy, think of the water as negative patterns you've been repeating and the mud that has accumulated in your life as a result. Scoop up all that nonsense and bring it behind you in this hypnotic and enjoyable meditation. You may find that this activity makes a lot of sense in its symbolism and its energetic effect. With the movement and chanting, you also change your frequency, so that you can attract different things in your life — that's one way to interpret "clearing karmas" in the meditation's title. And you guessed the other benefit: a stronger arcline.

MEDITATION FOR THE ARCLINE AND TO CLEAR THE KARMAS

August 1, 1996

Sit in Easy Pose with a straight spine and a light Neck Lock.

Mudra: Rest the elbows at the sides of the body. Extend the forearms forward parallel to the ground with hands facing up slightly cupped. Keeping the elbows bent, raise the arms up and back over the shoulders as far back as possible on each **"WHAA-HAY GUROO"** and **"WHAA-HAY JEEO"**. Immediately return to the starting position. (1 cycle per 2 seconds). The movement is as if scooping water and throwing it with a flick of the wrists over the shoulders and through the arcline.

Eye Focus: Closed.

Breath: Not specified.

Mantra: Listen to the mantra: **WHAA-HAY GUROO, WHAA-HAY GUROO, WHAA-HAY GUROO, WHAA-HAY JEEO** (A version by Gyani Ji was played in the original class.)

Time: 31 minutes.

To End: Inhale deeply, stretch the hands as far back as possible, suspend the breath **10-15 seconds**, exhale. Repeat **2 more times**.

Comments: This meditation is said to clear karmic memory that is held within the arcline. The power of Infinity is within you, not outside of you.

Breath In, Breath Out
Keep Up With Your Journey

HEAL YOURSELF

The message of today's meditation is simple: You can heal yourself. Nobody can do more good for you than yourself. If that sounds like the statement of a lonely person having to fend for themselves, you have forgotten the fundamental truth like so many people have: All your power is within your own self. Switch it on with this beautiful yogic tool.

MEDITATION FOR SELF-HEALING

May 23th, 2000

Sit in Easy Pose with a straight spine and a light Neck Lock.

Mudra: Firmly grasp the back of the neck with the left hand under any loose hair, the left elbow stretched to the side and upper arm parallel to the ground. Raise the right arm parallel to the ground and bend the elbow so that the hand is in front of the Heart Center, palm facing down and fingers together pointing to the left.

Eye Focus: Not specified.

Breath: Not specified.

Mantra: Chant the Siri Gaitri Mantra: **RAA MAA DAA SAA, SAA SAY SO HUNG**. (Slow version by Joseph Michael Levry was played in the original class).

Time: 17 minutes.

To End: Inhale deeply, suspend the breath for **25 seconds**, pull the neck forward and resist the pressure and keep the neck straight. Make the body like steel, circulate the energy throughout the body, to every organ, every cell, exhale. Repeat **2 more times** with the breath suspended for **10 seconds**.

FEEL BETTER ABOUT YOUR FUTURE RIGHT NOW

In Kundalini Yoga, the psychological state of fear is also called a non-reality. It makes a lot of sense: when we fear something, it's almost always an event or situation in the future that hasn't happened yet, it's just not real and may very well never be. Still, our thoughts and emotions about it are happening right now, like a huge dark cloud hanging over our present. We can remove this ghost of a non-existent future from our present experience with this meditation. If you master the one-minute breath in this meditation, keep this tool in your pocket and use it wherever you have some quiet time — on the train, waiting for a friend, before you go to sleep. Even without the mudra, the breath can do wonders in becoming calmer, healthier, and more intuitive.

MEDITATION TO REMOVE FEAR OF THE FUTURE

October 26, 1988

Sit in Easy Pose with a straight spine and a light Neck Lock.

Mudra: Place the left hand in the palm of the right hand. Grasp the left hand by curling the fingers of the right hand around the left hand and the right thumb on the left palm. Cross the left thumb over the right thumb. Hold this mudra gently at the Heart Center.

Eye Focus: Not specified.

Breath: Not specified.

Mantra: Meditate on your favorite version of the shabad **DHAN DHAN RAM DAS GUROO**.

Time: Start with **11 minutes** and slowly build to **31 minutes**.

To End: Inhale deeply, exhale. Repeat **2 more times**.

Comments: This meditation clears the fear of the future which has been created by your subconscious memories of the past. Without judgment, it connects you to the flow of life and to become conscious of the Self through your Heart Center. The mudra at the Heart Center awakens a peaceful, secure feeling.

UPGRADE YOUR COMPUTING POWER

Just as you upgrade your technology so it can keep up with the times, your brain's computing power depends on the quality of its hardware and software. This meditation is an upgrade for your frontal lobe, the youngest part of the brain that is also responsible for the most human and evolved qualities of the human being. With a highly functioning frontal lobe, you can cruise through this fast and ever-changing world with the ease and sophistication of a Ferrari. The debris from sexual violence does not become a roadblock, but just a curve in the road that you get by quickly. Give yourself the gift of top-notch brain power — a blessing of the self.

MEDITATION FOR BLESSING

April 21, 1997

PART ONE

Sit in Easy Pose with a straight spine and a light Neck Lock.

Mudra: Extend the Jupiter (index) and Saturn (middle) fingers, keeping the other fingers held down with the thumbs. Stretch the arms out to the sides, parallel to the ground with no bend in the elbows. Right hand is facing down and the left hand is facing up. Keep the spine steady.

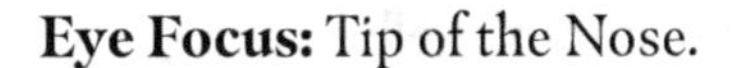

Eye Focus: Tip of the Nose.

Breath: Not specified.

Mantra: Listen to the mantra **WHAA-HAY GUROO, WHAA-HAY GUROO, WHAA-HAY GUROO, WHAA-HAY JEEO** (The recording by Gyani Ji was played in the original class.)

Time: 11 minutes.

To End: Inhale, suspend the breath for **20 seconds** and contract every vertebrae starting from the base to the top of the spine, then Cannon Fire exhale. Repeat **2 more times**.

Comments: As you look at the tip of your nose and the forehead feels heavy, it is working on the frontal lobe, which controls the personality. Let the energy flow. The words of the mantra are an affirmation, "God, take me from darkness to light." If Part One becomes too painful, you can chant the mantra to support you in keeping up.

PART TWO

Remain in Easy Pose.

Mudra: Stretch the arms forward and up at a 30 degree angle. The hands face down, with the fingers together and thumbs extended. The thumb tips touch. Keep the arms straight and stable with no bend in the elbows.

Eye Focus: Closed.

Breath: Not specified.

Mantra: Keep listening to the mantra **WHAA-HAY GUROO, WHAA-HAY GUROO, WHAA-HAY GUROO, WHAA-HAY JEEO**.

Time: 9 minutes.

To End: Inhale deeply, suspend the breath for **20 seconds**, make the body strong as steel, exhale. Repeat **2 more times**, suspending the breath for **10 seconds**.

Comments: Feel the healing flowing through the hands and bless the Earth. If you are a teacher, gracefully bless your students.

PART THREE

Remain in Easy Pose with
a firm Neck Lock.

Mudra: Place the left palm on the Navel Point, with the fingers pointing towards the right and press the navel. With the right elbow close to the body, raise the right hand as if taking a solemn oath, palm facing forward at the level of the shoulder. Press firmly on the Navel Point as you chant **HAR** powerfully.

Eye Focus: Stare straight forward.

Breath: Not specified.

Mantra: Chant **HAR** one per second.

Time: 3 ½ minutes.

PART FOUR

Remain in Easy Pose.

Mudra: Maintain the mudra as in Part Three. Turn to a person and place the right palms together with enough pressure to keep the right palms in the middle, between partners. Press the Navel Point with the left hand with firm pressure. Apply equal pressure on both hands. If practicing alone, imagine you are pressing another person's hand.

Eye Focus: Look straight into
the eyes of the partner.

Breath: Not specified.

Mantra: Chant **HAR** powerfully once per second as you press the fingers into the navel. (The recording "Rhythms of Gatka" by Matamandir Singh was played during the original class.)

Time: 1 minute. Immediately begin Part Five.

PART FIVE

Remain in the position in Part Four.

Eye Focus: Closed.

Breath: Long Deep Breathing.

Mental Focus: Meditate deeply, become absolutely thoughtless and hypnotize yourself. Receive the heavens, into the total energy of God.

Music: In the original class "Sat Nam, Wahe Guru #3" by Lata Mangeshkar was played for **20 ½ minutes** and then "Flowers in the Rain", live on guitar by Gurudass Singh of Spain for **7 minutes.**

Total Time: 27 ½ minutes.

To End: Relax and stretch every part of the body.

Comments: After this meditation series, it is recommended to drink a lot of lemon water to cleanse what has been released through this meditation.

Breath In, Breath Out
Keep Up With Your Journey

TRANSCEND YOUR BOUNDARIES

If you wanted to describe yoga in one sentence, this could be it: "Understanding and experiencing that you are one with everything". And why does it matter? When you truly feel that you are connected to the whole universe and everything in it, you feel seen, heard, supported, and protected. It's hard to feel lonely, isolated and fearful when that is your lived experience. In that sense, yoga is not just the key to true happiness for anyone, but also the perfect antidote to the negative effects of sexual violence, which almost always includes isolation and fear. The purpose of this meditation is the expansion of the self beyond your physical boundaries and into the Universe. Do it with the intention to break out of your shell and merge into the universe and its main ingredient — love.

MEDITATION FOR MENTAL CONTROL
BRAHM KALAA KRIYA

Originally published in I Am A Woman Essential Kriyas

Sit in Easy Pose with a straight spine and a light Neck Lock.

Mudra: Stretch the arms forward, bend the elbows and place the right forearm on top of the left forearm, hands facing down with the fingers together and straight. The upper arms and forearms are parallel to the ground. Stretch the arms out from the shoulders as much as possible. Find balance in this position.

Eye Focus: Closed.

Breath: The breath will naturally become slow.

Time: Begin with **3 minutes** and gradually build to **11 minutes**.

Comments: In this kriya, it's as though you were extending your Self out into the Universe.

ACTIVATE YOUR GLANDS FOR BETTER HEALTH AND SLEEP

A well-functioning glandular system makes you feel good on every level by orchestrating your body chemistry to support you in any situation. This meditation activates a chemical mix that gives you relaxation, rejuvenation, and healing. It's a great example of the power of controlled breath, and you might feel the soothing effects after just a few moments.

REJUVENATION MEDITATION

April 12, 1979

Sit in Easy Pose with a straight spine and a light Neck Lock.

Mudra: Place the upper arms and elbows firmly on the rib cage and raise the forearms bringing the sides of the hands together at the center of the chest, palms facing up. The outer sides of the Mercury (little) fingers touch and the other fingers and thumbs are spread apart. The hands are slightly cupped.

Eye Focus: Focus the eyes past the tip of the nose to the distant ground and beyond into the depths of the Earth.

Breath & Mantra: Inhale deeply and slowly through the mouth through semi-puckered lips, and suspend the breath for **4 seconds** as you mentally chant the mantra **SAA TAA NAA MAA**. Exhale completely in **4 strokes** through the nose as you mentally chant the mantra **SAA TAA NAA MAA** (1 syllable per stroke). Suspend the breath out for **2 seconds** as you mentally chant **WHAA-HAY GUROO**.

Time: 11-31 minutes maximum.

Comments: This is a potent meditation for the glandular system. Its effects are strong enough to help your system fight disease. It does not replace allopathic forms of medicine, but it does open the healing and preventative capacity of your body. The meditation focuses its effects on the glandular system, the guardians of your health. Start slowly; it is best to practice before going to bed as it can make you spacey.

Breath In, Breath Out
Keep Up With Your Journey

ELEVATE YOUR SPIRIT BY ADJUSTING YOUR BODY

Yes, it can be as simple as that, your emotional state can change completely if you put your body in new positions. Usually we think of our emotions and our related body language as automatic reactions to circumstances. For example, if you find yourself in a depressing situation, your shoulders might sag and your chin drop down. Most people might stay here until the depressing situation ends. Not us yogis, because we know that change happens from the inside. So we flip a switch on the inside with the intention to feel better in spite of all circumstances, and then we reverse the physical process: we lift our shoulders, raise our chin, and voila: we've created a new vessel for an elevated spirit. This kriya optimizes this simple process with a series of vigorous movements that add up emotionally to get you into high spirits without having to change anything else in your environment. The kriya also features several classic Kundalini asanas, so you'll meet some good friends on the way to your natural high.

BODY ADJUSTMENT TO ELEVATE THE SPIRIT

July 2, 1984

1) Leg Lifts. Lie on the back with the legs together, interlace the fingers and place them under the neck. Raise both legs up to 90 degrees on the inhale and lower the legs down on the exhale. Keep the legs together and straight. Continue for **54-108 repetitions**. *This exercise strengthens the abdominal muscles and supports the digestive process.*

2) Serabandanda Variation. On your hands and knees, hands under the shoulders and knees under the hips, lift the pelvis by straightening the arms and legs and come into Triangle Pose. Distribute the weight evenly on the hands and feet. Inhale and move slowly into Cobra Pose, arching the back, bringing the pelvis to the ground, tops of the feet on the ground, lifting the chest while keeping the arms straight. Exhale and go back into Triangle Pose. Move smoothly from one posture to the other with the breath for **26-52 repetitions**. *This exercise creates a safe stretch for all of the tissues around the nerves in the body, helping the nerves to fire more efficiently. Also the shifting of the torso from upside down to right side up helps to flush the cerebrospinal fluid around the brain and spinal cord.*

3) Life Nerve Stretch. Sit with the legs stretched forward, a straight spine and a light Neck Lock. Grasp the toes of both feet, inhale and elongate the spine, exhale and stretch down, bringing the chest to the knees. Heart leads and the head follows. Inhale, come up to the center. Hands hold the toes throughout the movement. Continue for **54-108 repetitions**. Breathe powerfully.
This exercise stretches the hamstrings, the sciatic nerve and urinary bladder meridian.

4) Spinal Twist in Rock Pose. Sit on the heels in Rock Pose with a straight spine and a light Neck Lock. Interlock the fingers behind the head at the hairline under any loose hair. Twist to the left on the inhale and twist to the right on the exhale. Keep the upper arms parallel to the ground, elbows pulled back to open the chest. Initiate the movement from the Navel Point, not the arms. The head moves last. Continue for **54-108 repetitions** to each side.
This exercise helps to move the lymph fluid through the lymph vessels and lymph nodes. This vigorous movement creates a flushing action for the aura, moving out old stagnant energy. It activates and flushes the spleen through a meridian point beneath the armpit.

5) Cat-Cow. Come onto the hands and knees, with palms on the ground directly underneath the shoulders and knees directly underneath the hips. Inhale and arch your back downward, lowering the belly, lifting the sternum and chin and broadening the collarbones. Keep the back of the neck elongated. Exhale and round your spine upward, bringing the chin to the chest. Use the hands and knees as a firm base of support for the spine. Keep the arms straight. Maintain a steady rhythm for **54-108 repetitions.** *This is a complete movement for the spine. It helps keep all segments relaxed and mobile.*

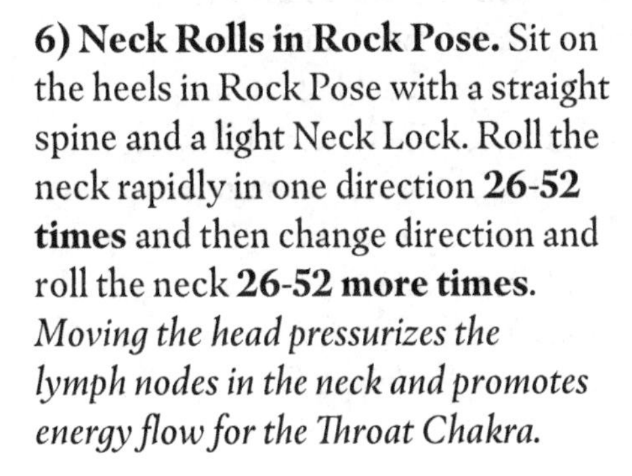

6) Neck Rolls in Rock Pose. Sit on the heels in Rock Pose with a straight spine and a light Neck Lock. Roll the neck rapidly in one direction **26-52 times** and then change direction and roll the neck **26-52 more times**. *Moving the head pressurizes the lymph nodes in the neck and promotes energy flow for the Throat Chakra.*

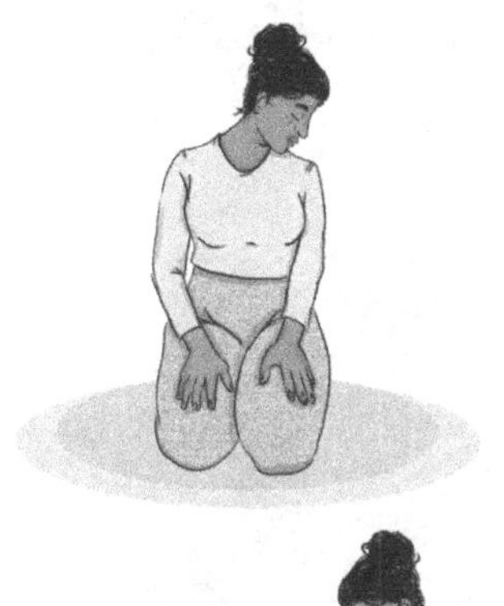

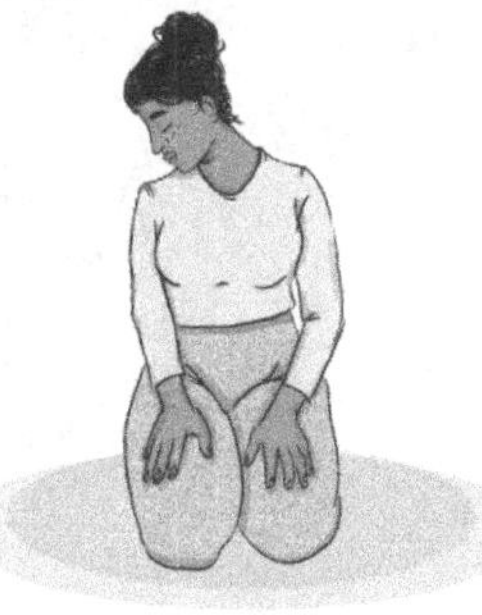

7) Side Bends in Rock Pose. Remain in Rock Pose and rest the hands on the thighs. Bend from the waist side to side. As you bend to the right, stretch the left arm over the head, and as you bend to the left stretch the right arm. Bend completely, stretching a little further with each bend. Continue for **26-52 repetitions** to each side.
This exercise is for the liver, spleen, and colon. Side bends pressurize the liver, helping move blood through the organ and support its role of detoxifying, clearing hormones, and balancing the blood.

8) Arms Pulling with Chanting. Remain in Rock Pose and reach one arm forward as if reaching out and grabbing energy. Then pull it back in, while reaching forward with the other arm. Move rapidly and chant the mantra **SAA TAA NAA MAA** (1 syllable on the extension of each arm) for **5 minutes.**
This exercise pushes lymph fluid and cleanses the chest area. Physical movement coordinated with breath and the Bij mantra balances all tattvas.

9) Sufi Grinds. Sit in Easy Pose with a straight spine and a light Neck Lock. Place the hands on the knees. Lift the rib cage to open the space between the rib cage and the pelvis. Rotate the pelvis, inhaling as the pelvis circles forward and exhaling as the pelvis circles backwards. Only the pelvis, lower spine and abdomen move; the rib cage, shoulders, neck and head stay stable. Continue for **3 minutes**. *Churning motion of the torso in this exercise supports moving food through the digestive tract. Gentle motion of the spine helps to release blocks or muscle tightness.*

10) Relaxation. Lie down on the back in Corpse Pose and relax for **11 minutes**. (The gong was played in the original class.)

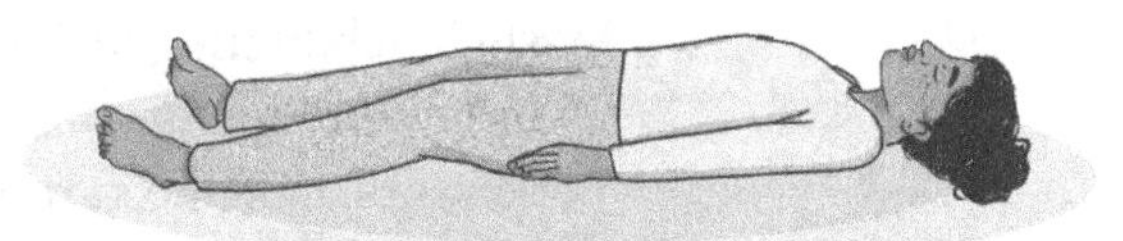

Comments: This kriya maintains the body's vitality. By adjusting the body, you can elevate your spirit.

DELETE OLD BELIEFS FOR NEW EXPERIENCES

One of the most satisfying things in life is having a new experience. That is why we want to open closed doors and go on adventures. Crucial for any healthy exploration is the underlying belief that, despite some challenges and bumps on the road, we will be ok in the end. Sexual violence can rob you of fundamental optimism and instead plant a belief in your suboncsious that unknown equals harm. With such a belief living inside you unchecked, you are cut off from newness and the liveliness and expansion that come from embracing the unknown. This meditation removes the energetic ties to such debilitating beliefs to allow newness into your life. As your fingers move like scissors, imagine cutting these old beliefs like wilted flowers from your garden of life.

MEDITATION OPEN TO NEWNESS IN YOU

April 5, 2000

Sit in Easy Pose with a straight spine and a light Neck Lock.

Mudra: Extend the Jupiter (index) and Saturn (middle) fingers, keeping the other fingers held down with the thumbs. Relax the elbows at the sides of the body and raise the forearms perpendicular to the ground. The hands are at shoulder level with the palms facing forward and fingers pointing up. Open and close the Jupiter and Saturn fingers in a scissor-like motion. Create a steady rhythm.

Eye Focus: Closed.

Breath: Not specified for the first **20 minutes**. Powerfully inhale and exhale through the "O" mouth moving the navel with the breath for **2 ½ more minutes**.

Mental Focus: Concentrate on the movement of the 2 fingers, cutting self-negating subconscious thoughts.

Total Time: 22 ½ minutes.

To End: Inhale deeply, suspend the breath for **15 seconds**, pull the navel towards the spine, Cannon Fire exhale. Repeat **2 more times**.

Comments: When the fingers come together, the subconscious thoughts you have against yourself will fly away.

COMMUNICATE CLEARLY WITH YOURSELF AND THE UNIVERSE

We can know a great deal about a person without hearing them speak or having any other information about them besides their presence. Their presence is a projection of their particular mix of thoughts, beliefs, opinions, intentions and psychological states. We can read their presence depending on our level of sensitivity, but it's often pretty easy to sense if something inside of them is off, even if they are not aware of it themselves. We can often also carry inner conflicts. Examples are desires that clash with your beliefs, or obligations you don't want to fulfill, and of course the conflict you find yourself in when sexual violence affects your life or involves someone you know. Whether you are aware of the details of your inner conflict or not, you'll feel the discomfort nonetheless. This meditation can sort inner conflicts out for you and put you back into a state of harmony and consistency, so that you can focus and find solutions that are aligned with your whole being.

MEDITATION TO ELIMINATE INNER CONFLICTS

October 24, 2000

Sit in Easy Pose with a straight spine and a light Neck Lock.

Mudra: Interlace the fingers in Venus Lock and place the hands in front of the solar plexus with the palms facing the body.

Eye Focus: Closed.

Breath: Not specified.

Mantra: Chant **HUMEE HUM BRAHM HUM** (The recording by Nirinjan Kaur was played in the original class.)

Time: 22 minutes.

To End: Inhale deeply, suspend the breath for **15 seconds**, exhale. Repeat **2 more times**.

Comments: Listen to the mantra and meditate on the meaning of the words: "We are We, We are God." When you understand this mantra, inner conflict is eliminated.

BEGIN TO TRUST AGAIN

This meditation returns peace to your inner world as do most of the previous meditations in their own particular way, and with this one trust is the main focus. Trust in life, in yourself, in the goodness of the world and the people around you can all be shattered when you experience sexual violece. Despite everything that might have happened in the past, allow yourself to trust again. Do it for your own sake, so that you can stand on solid ground again. You just cannot move forward without trust. If it's hard for you, or if you need help building your trust, practice this meditation and open yourself up to the capacity for trust in the whole universe.

MEDITATION FOR BHROSA

Originally published in Sadhana Guidelines

Sit in Easy Pose or Lotus Pose with a straight spine and a light Neck Lock.

Mudra: Raise the arms to form an arc over the head with the palms facing down, with the elbows slightly bent. For working with masculine, projective energy, place the right on top of the left. For working feminine, reflective energy, place the left on top of the right. Touch the tips of the thumbs together, pointing backward.

Eye Focus: 1/10th open,
look at the upper lip.

Breath: Not specified.

Mantra: Whisper softly so that the last word is almost inaudible. **WHAA-HAY GUROO** (2 ½ seconds per repetition.)

Time: 11 minutes.

Comments: Use the lips and tongue to precisely form each sound. This meditation affects the element of trust in the human personality. Trust is the basis of faith and commitment and the sense of reality. It will give you the elevation of spirit so you can stand up to any challenge. It builds and balances the aura from the Fourth Chakra up. In time, you may increase 1 minute every 15 days, until you reach 31 minutes maximum.

CONFIRM YOUR TRUST IN PEOPLE AND THE UNIVERSE

It is no coincidence that our program for healing sexual violence ends with two meditations for trust. Trust is the consistent belief that things will work out for the best. Trust in a person is the consistent belief that they will not harm you. A healthy and happy life is built on the belief that, for the most part, the world lives up to these beliefs. The alternative would be a life in fear, in anticipation of harm and misfortune. We want you to have a strong positive belief. We cannot guarantee that everything will always be easy, but you need to have trust – often despite the signals you receive from the physical world – because that is the key for a strong spirit and true well being. Solidify your trust in everything with this meditation.

MEDITATION TO DEVELOP TRUST

March 10, 1977

Sit in Easy Pose with a straight spine and a light Neck Lock.

Mudra: Stretch the arms out to the sides parallel to the ground, bend the elbows so that the forearms are perpendicular to the ground and at a 90-degree angle from the upper arms. Curl the fingers onto the mounds at the base of the fingers and pull the knuckles back, stretching the palms wide. Draw the thumbs away from the fingers and point them straight back. Keep the spine lifted and straight with a light navel engagement, and lean back from the hips as far as possible. Stretch the diaphragm area. Keep a balance with the arms.

Eye Focus: 1/10th open.

Breath: Inhale in 4 equal strokes, mentally chanting **SO** on each stroke, and exhale in 4 equal strokes, mentally chanting **HUNG** on each stroke.

Mantra: **SO SO SO SO, HUNG HUNG HUNG HUNG**

Time: 3 minutes maximum.

To End: Inhale, suspend the breath and stretch the arms straight up, exhale, suspend and bend forward from the hips, resting the head and upper body on the ground.

Comments: This is a very powerful exercise. It is a super transcendental meditation. Whether or not you understand what meditation is, it is not important. Get into the posture and let God take care of you.

ADDITIONAL RESOURCES

Brown, Brené. *Rising Strong: How the Ability to Reset Transforms the Way We Live, Love, Parent, and Lead.* New York: Random House, 2017.

Estés, Clarissa Pinkola. *Women Who Run With the Wolves: Myths and Stories of the Wild Woman Archetype.* New York: Ballantine Books, 1992.

Gračanin, A., Bylsma, L. M., & Vingerhoets, A. J. (2014). Is crying a self-soothing behavior?. *Frontiers in Psychology*, 5, 502. https://doi.org/10.3389/fpsyg.2014.00502

"How to Report Rape and Sexual Assault". Advice and Information from United Kingdom Metropolitan Police.

https://www.met.police.uk/advice/advice-and-information/rsa/rape-and-sexual-assault/how-to-report-rape-and-sexual-assault/, n.d. Accessed June 10, 2022.

"Report of the Independent Review into The Investigation and Prosecution of Rape in London by Rt Hon Dame Elish Angiolini DBE QC | The Crown Prosecution Service." www.cps.gov.uk. Accessed June 10, 2022. https://www.cps.gov.uk/publication/report-independent-review-investigation-and-prosecution-rape-london-rt-hon-dame-elish.

"Support for Victims of Rape and Sexual Assault". Advice and Information from the United Kingdom Metropolitan Police. https://www.met.police.uk/advice/advice-and-information/rsa/rape-and-sexual-assault/support-for-victims-of-rape-and-sexual-assault/

US National Sexual Assault Online Hotline: 800.656. HOPE or http://online.rainn.org Accessed June 10, 2022.

"US Rape, Abuse & Incest National Network (RAINN) - The Nation's Largest Anti-Sexual Violence Organization." www.rainn.org. Accessed June 10, 2022. https://www.rainn.org/.

"What is rape and sexual assault". Advice and Information from United Kingdom Metropolitan Police. https://www.met.police.uk/advice/advice-and-information/rsa/rape-and-sexual-assault/what-is-rape-and-sexual-assault/

ABOUT THE AUTHOR

Simranjeet Kaur, also known as Jackie Wakeford-Smith, joined the Metropolitan Police Service in London in the late 80s to serve and protect the public in the city's streets when very few women did. As part of her policing career she was trained as a specialised Sexual Offences Interview Technique Officer (SOIT). Later in her career, she led a team of detectives, dedicated solely to the investigation of rape and serious sexual assaults. Her training, knowledge and experience was developed over many years of dealing with individuals, as both victims and perpetrators. During her last years of service she dealt with over one thousand cases, each of them left its own imprint and impact on Simranjeet's physical and subtle bodies, which resulted in her suffering from secondary traumatic stress. This reminded her of the famous principle of Dr. Edmond Locard, a 19th-century French criminologist, which states that every contact leaves a trace.

In 2015, as she got close to retirement, the compounded stress led to a collapse of her body and mind. "Battling the effects of prolonged trauma and compassion fatigue, I hit the dark night of the Soul", she shares. That's when she started to practice Kundalini Yoga for her own healing process. She describes its effects as the opening of a floodgate of joy and ecstasy. Her immersion into the practice later led her to becoming a Kundalini Yoga teacher and trainer.

During her recovery and healing journey, Jackie saw the parallels between her trauma and those of the victims of sexual violence: for instance, how it feels to be in a world that most don't talk about; to be alone with the haunting memories of severe traumatic incidents; the anger, guilt, all of the psychological effects of these crimes; and the devastating effects on individuals, families and communities. Having used Kundalini Yoga for her own recovery process from prolonged secondary traumatic stress, Simranjeet was inspired to share these amazing yogic tools in the form of this beautiful book: a 40-day program using yoga and meditation to find peace within shattered pieces.

Simranjeet Kaur has been practicing, studying and teaching Kundalini Yoga since 2009. The Kundalini Research Institute and the British Complementary Medical Association have endorsed her work.

KRI PUBLICATIONS

KRI
• SINCE 1972 •

CPSIA information can be obtained
at www.ICGtesting.com
Printed in the USA
JSHW021412280922
31074JS00002B/3

9 780963 984791